Working Words in
SPELLING

G. Willard Woodruff and George N. Moore

with Robert G. Forest • Richard A. Talbot • Ann R. Talbot

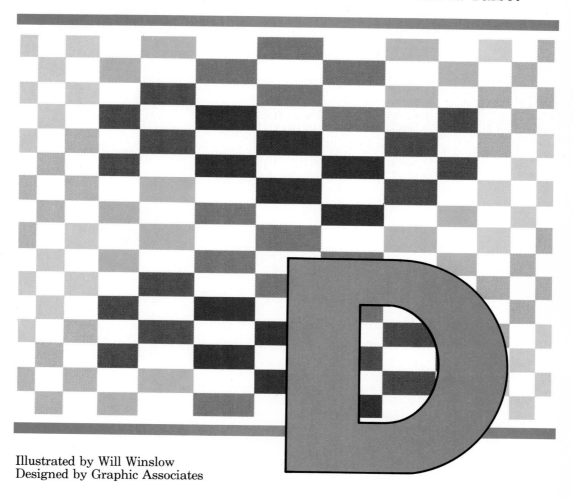

Illustrated by Will Winslow
Designed by Graphic Associates

D.C. Heath and Company
Lexington, Massachusetts/Toronto, Canada

Become a S-H-A-R-P Speller

See the word.
- Look at the word.
- Think about the letters that spell the word.

Hear the word.
- Say the word.
- Listen to the consonant and vowel sounds.

Adopt the word.
- Close your eyes.
- See the word in your mind's eye.
- Think about how it looks and sounds.

Record the word.
- Cover the word.
- Write the word.

Proofread the word.
- Correct the word.
- Touch each letter.
- Think about the word again.

SPELLEX®—a registered trademark of Curriculum Associates, Inc.
SPELLEX® Glossary incorporated by permission of Curriculum Associates, Inc.
Handwriting models in this book are reproduced with permission of Zaner-Bloser, Inc., from the series *HANDWRITING: Basic Skills and Application,* ©1984.
Copyright ©1988 by D.C. Heath and Company
Published simultaneously in Canada
Printed in the United States of America
International Standard Book Number: 0-669-15457-1
                    4 5 6 7 8 9 0

a. ☐☐☐

b. ☐☐☐

c. ☐☐☐

d. ☐☐☐☐☐

I. Check Test. Write each spelling word.

e. ☐☐☐

II. Spelling Words and Phrases

f. ☐☐☐☐

fade	will **fade** in the light
wade	to **wade** into the water
cape	wool **cape**
races	relay **races**
dare	if you **dare**
he's	if **he's** ready
she's	if **she's** going
being	**being** very unkind
meet	will **meet** at the game
seemed	**seemed** to know
mile	one **mile** away
pile	**pile** of sand
dive	a shallow **dive**
size	a different **size**
alike	look **alike**
hire	will **hire** the student

g. ☐☐☐☐

h. ☐☐☐☐

i. ☐☐☐☐

j. ☐☐☐

k. ☐☐☐☐☐

l. ☐☐☐☐

m. ☐☐☐

n. ☐☐☐☐

o. ☐☐☐☐

p. ☐☐☐

Other Word Forms

faded, fading, wades, waded, wading, capes, race, raced, racing, dares, dared, daring, be, been, am, is, met, meeting, seem, seems, seeming, miles, piles, piled, piling, dives, dived, dove, diving, diver, sizes, alikeness, hired, hiring

3

IV. All in a Row.
Write the sixteen spelling words in alphabetical order. Then join the boxed letters and write four hidden words.

1. — — — □ —
2. — — — □ —
3. — — — □
4. — — — □

Hidden Word: _____

5. □ — — —
6. — — — □
7. — □ , —
8. — — □ —

Hidden Word: _____

9. — — — □
10. — □ — —
11. — — — □
12. — — — — □

Hidden Word: _____

13. □ — — — , — — —
14. — □ — —
15. — — — □
16. — — □ —

Hidden Word: _____

V. What Am I?
Solve each word mystery with a spelling word.

a. I'm a walk in the water. — — — —

b. I'm 5,280 feet. — — — —

c. I'm a sleeveless coat. — — — —

d. I'm a favorite of fast runners. — — — — —

e. I'm a leap into water. — — — —

f. I'm a heap of things. — — — —

g. I'm a 15 shirt or a 12 dress. — — — —

h. I'm a challenge. — — — —

FINISH

Spelling Words

fade   wade   cape   races   dare   he's   she's   being
meet   seemed   mile   pile   dive   size   alike   hire

VI. Crossword Puzzle. Solve the puzzle by using words from the spelling list. Check your answers in the **Glossary/SPELLEX®**.

Across
2. to dim
5. acting in a certain way
6. appeared
8. he is (contraction)

Down
1. to pay for work
3. similar
4. she is (contraction)
7. to come together

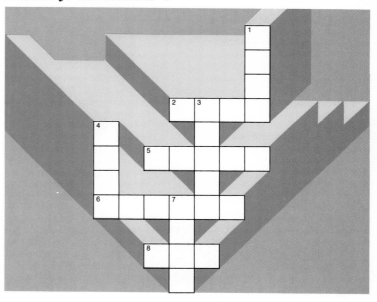

VII. Finding Words. The words in the spelling list appear in the beginning (A-H), middle (I-Q), or end (R-Z) of the **Glossary/SPELLEX®**. Write each word.

Beginning A-H	Middle I-Q	End R-Z
1. _____	1. _____	1. _____
2. _____	2. _____	2. _____
3. _____	3. _____	3. _____
4. _____		4. _____
5. _____		5. _____
6. _____		
7. _____		
8. _____		

5

VIII. Writing Sentences. Write each set of words in a sentence. You may use **Other Word Forms** (p. 3).

1. he's—pile

2. she's—cape

3. alike—size

4. being—dive

5. meet—races

6. hire—mile

7. seemed—fade

8. dare—wade

IX. Final Test. Write each spelling word.

I. Check Test. Write each spelling word.

II. Spelling Words and Phrases

woke	**woke** up early
holes	**holes** in my socks
won't	**won't** try again
tore	**tore** the shirt
wore	**wore** old clothes
ax	sharpened the **ax**
rack	storage **rack**
backward	**backward** somersault
draft	a cold **draft**
can't	**can't** argue about it
camel	**camel** in the desert
madly	was running **madly**
began	**began** all over
mapping	**mapping** the city
crossing	**crossing** the street
across	**across** and down

III. Find a Fit. Write each word in its correct shape.

a.

b.

c.

d.

e.

f.

g.

h.

i.

j.

k.

l.

m.

n.

o.

p.

Other Word Forms

wake, waking, wakes, hole, torn, tear, tears, tearing, wear, wears, wearing, worn, axes, racks, backwards, drafts, camels, mad, madder, maddest, begin, begins, beginning, map, maps, mapped, cross, crosses, crossed

7

IV. Missing Vowels. Find the missing vowels and write the spelling words.

a. dr __ ft   _____

b. c __ m __ l   _____

c. m __ pp __ ng   _____

d. w __ r __   _____

e. b __ g __ n   _____

f. w __ k __   _____

g. cr __ ss __ ng   _____

h. b __ ckw __ rd   _____

i. h __ l __ s   _____

j. c __ n't   _____

k. w __ n't   _____

l. __ cr __ ss   _____

m. t __ r __   _____

n. m __ dl __   _____

o. __ x   _____

p. r __ ck   _____

V. Hide and Seek. The spelling words can be found in the word puzzle. The words appear across and down. Circle and write the words.

```
b  e  g  a  n  t  c  w  o
a  c  e  x  s  s  r  o  m
c  a  n  t  o  t  o  r  e
k  m  a  d  l  y  s  e  n
w  e  a  c  r  o  s  s  t
a  l  m  a  p  p  i  n  g
r  a  c  k  w  o  n  t  e
d  r  a  f  t  d  g  o  o
h  o  l  e  s  w  o  k  e
```

Across

1.
2.
3.
4.
5.
6.
7.
8.
9.
10.
11.

Down

1.
2.
3.
4.
5.

Spelling Words

woke holes won't tore wore ax rack backward draft can't camel madly began mapping crossing across

VI. Word Riddles. Write the spelling word that answers each riddle.

a. Making a plan of your neighborhood _____

b. What the nail did to your pants _____

c. What clothes hang on _____

d. An animal that is handy in the desert _____

e. What you dug in the ground _____

f. The opposite of *forward* _____

g. The first thing you did this morning _____

h. What you used to cut a tree _____

i. Where you and a chicken went on the road _____

j. What you did when you started _____

k. How you worked when in a rush _____

l. The opposite of *will* _____

m. The opposite of *can* _____

n. A cool place you try to avoid _____

o. What you should be doing to all your *t*'s _____

p. What you did with your new sweater _____

9

VII. Finding Words. The words in the spelling list appear in the beginning (A-H), middle (I-Q), or end (R-Z) of the **Glossary/SPELLEX®**. Write each word.

	Beginning A-H		Middle I-Q		End R-Z
1.	_____	1.	_____	1.	_____
2.	_____	2.	_____	2.	_____
3.	_____			3.	_____
4.	_____			4.	_____
5.	_____			5.	_____
6.	_____				
7.	_____				
8.	_____				
9.	_____				

VIII. All in a Sentence. Use each of the spelling words or **Other Word Forms** (p. 7) in sentences about a parade or a circus. Circle the spelling words and the other word forms you used.

<u>A Day at the Circus</u>

Example: *The clown* (wore) *a* (torn) *shirt.*

IX. Final Test. Write each spelling word.

10

Lesson 3

I. Check Test. Write each spelling word.

II. Spelling Words and Phrases

sum	a **sum** of money
plum	a ripe **plum**
lump	**lump** of clay
lung	a **lung** illness
hunter	**hunter** in the woods
begun	had **begun** adding
lace	**lace** tablecloth
fate	the **fate** of wild animals
cases	**cases** of books
saves	**saves** stamps
didn't	**didn't** even know
it's	if **it's** possible
itself	the job **itself**
swift	**swift** motion
begin	will **begin** to wonder
enter	will **enter** the race

III. Find a Fit. Write each word in its correct shape.

a.
b.
c.
d.
e.
f.
g.
h.
i.
j.
k.
l.
m.
n.
o.
p.

Other Word Forms

sums, summed, summary, plums, lumpy, lumps, lungs, hunt, hunts, began, begins, beginning, lace, laces, lacing, laced, lacy, fates, case, save, saved, saving, swiftest, swiftly, enters, entrance

IV. Scrambled Words. Unscramble the scrambled word to find the spelling word that completes the sentence. Write the word.

  a. The race is about to _____ .   binge

  b. He has a small _____ on his head.   mpul

  c. Careful driving _____ lives.   svase

  d. A prune is a dried _____ .   umpl

  e. _____ time for the mail carrier to come.   t'is

  f. The banker has a large _____ of money.   ums

  g. We have not _____ to fight.   unbeg

  h. Put the blankets in the cardboard _____ .   asecs

  i. _____ can play foolish games with a person.   feat

  j. Kindergarten children can _____ their own shoes.   cale

  k. You must _____ from the side door.   renet

  l. The gill of a fish is similar to a _____ .   ungl

  m. The door appeared to open by _____ .   elfist

  n. The batter is a _____ runner.   ftisw

  o. The dogs _____ bark last night.   n'tidd

  p. The _____ circled the woods.   herunt

V. Finding Words. The words in the spelling list appear in the beginning (A-H), middle (I-Q), or end (R-Z) of the **Glossary/SPELLEX®**. Write each word.

Beginning A-H	Middle I-Q	End R-Z
1. _____	1. _____	1. _____
2. _____	2. _____	2. _____
3. _____	3. _____	3. _____
4. _____	4. _____	
5. _____	5. _____	
6. _____	6. _____	
7. _____		

Spelling Words

sum   plum   lump   lung   hunter   begun   lace   fate
cases   saves   didn't   it's   itself   swift   begin   enter

VI. Lines That Rhyme. Write a set of lines that rhyme. The first line in each set is done for you. Use a spelling word or an **Other Word Form** (p. 11) in the second line.

a. He had to <u>jump</u>

_____

b. She pounded the <u>drum</u>

_____

c. If he is <u>late</u>

_____

d. The boat began to <u>drift</u>

_____

e. The song was <u>sung</u>

_____

f. If she plans to <u>win</u>

_____

g. All kinds of <u>faces</u>

_____

h. We started to <u>hum</u>

_____

i. It was a strange <u>case</u>

_____

j. We stood in the <u>center</u>

_____

k. They all began to <u>run</u>

_____

l. There was a space on the <u>shelf</u>

_____

m. A joke or a <u>stunt</u>

_____

n. They entered the <u>cave</u>

_____

What two spelling words had no rhyming words?

_____   _____

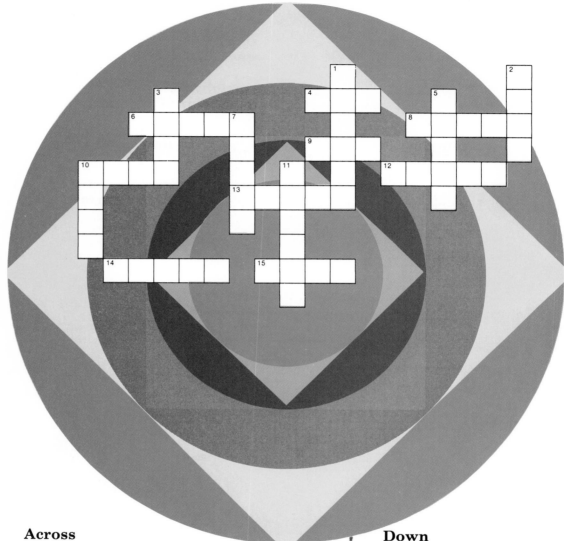

Across

4. the answer when you add numbers
6. boxes
8. started
9. it is (contraction)
10. to tie with string
12. fast
13. to come in
14. did not (contraction)
15. a fruit

Down

1. a person who searches
2. an organ for breathing
3. what happens to a person
5. to start
7. protects from danger
10. a bump
11. The cat washed _____ .

VIII. Final Test. Write each spelling word.

14

Lesson 4

I. Check Test. Write each spelling word.

II. Spelling Words and Phrases

knee	bruised my **knee**
knot	untied the **knot**
knew	**knew** what to do
knows	**knows** the way
knife	the sharpest **knife**
prize	first or second **prize**
prices	high **prices**
shine	the **shine** of new paint
smile	made them **smile**
slide	long, steep **slide**
slid	**slid** across the ice
slip	will **slip** on the playground
grip	a firm **grip**
spin	to **spin** in the air
history	studied town **history**
arithmetic	a page of **arithmetic**

III. Find a Fit. Write each word in its correct shape.

a.

b.

c.

d.

e.

f.

g.

h.

i.

j.

k.

l.

m.

n.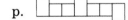

o.

p.

Other Word Forms

knees, kneel, knots, knotted, knotting, know, known, knowing, knives, knifing, prizes, price, shines, shined, shining, shiny, shinier, smiled, smiling, slides, sliding, slider, slips, slipped, slippery, grips, gripping, spins, spinning, spun, histories, historical, arithmetical

IV. Be a Sentence Detective. Complete the sentences with words from the spelling list.

a. She once _____ how to tie a _____ .

b. She easily added the _____ of the groceries because she was good
at _____ .

c. A lucky _____ of the top will win the _____ .

d. He _____ the answer now that he has read his _____ book.

e. On the playground be careful not to _____ off the _____ .

f. The butcher had a firm _____ on the sharp _____ .

g. Put a _____ on your face and a _____ on your shoes.

h. When she _____ down the tree, she skinned her _____ .

V. Sort Your Words. Write each spelling word. A word may go in more
than one column.

Words With One Syllable	Words With Two, Three, or Four Syllables	Words With Silent _k_
1. _____	1. _____	1. _____
2. _____	2. _____	2. _____
3. _____	3. _____	3. _____
4. _____		4. _____
5. _____		5. _____
6. _____		
7. _____		
8. _____		
9. _____		
10. _____		
11. _____		
12. _____		
13. _____		

16

Spelling Words

*knee knot knew knows knife prize prices shine
smile slide slid slip grip spin history arithmetic*

VI. Words and Meanings. Write a spelling word for each meaning. Check your answers in the **Glossary/SPELLEX®**.

a. was sure of the facts _____

b. moved easily _____

c. a record of past events _____

d. a tight hold _____

e. is sure of the facts _____

f. a fastening made with string _____

g. costs _____

h. a leg joint _____

i. brightness _____

j. to move easily _____

k. a sharp cutting tool _____

l. a happy look on a person's face _____

m. an award _____

n. to slide suddenly without control _____

o. adding and subtracting _____

p. to turn around quickly _____

17

VII. Writing Sentences. Write each set of words in a sentence. You may use **Other Word Forms** (p. 15).

1. history—arithmetic
2. prices—prize
3. grip—knows
4. knife—knot
5. slid—knee
6. slip—slide
7. spin—shine
8. smile—knew

VIII. Final Test. Write each spelling word.

Lesson 5

I. Check Test. Write each spelling word.

II. Spelling Words and Phrases

blade	the skate **blade**
blame	took all the **blame**
blaze	sudden **blaze**
brave	is **brave** to try
shake	felt the earth **shake**
stake	tied to a **stake**
skate	only one roller **skate**
scale	sang the **scale**
lend	will **lend** the book
bend	might **bend** the nail
melt	saw it **melt** away
deck	walked around the **deck**
flock	gathered the **flock**
shock	a **shock** from the lamp
blocks	cement **blocks**
pocket	jingled in my **pocket**

III. Find a Fit. Write each word in its correct shape.

a.
b.
c.
d.
e.
f.
g.
h.
i.
j.
k.
l.
m.
n.
o.
p.

Other Word Forms
blades, blames, blamed, blaming, blazes, blazing, braver, bravest, bravely, shaky, shakes, shook, shaking, stakes, staked, staking, skates, skated, skating, scales, lends, lending, bends, bent, bending, melts, melted, melting, decks, flocks, flocked, flocking, shocks, shocked, shocking, block, blocked, blocking, pockets

IV. Hide and Seek. The spelling words can be found in the word puzzle. The words appear across and down. Circle and write the words.

Across

1.
2.
3.
4.
5.
6.
7.
8.
9.
10.

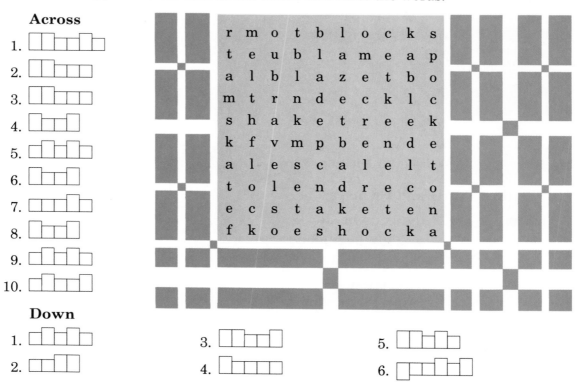

r m o t b l o c k s
t e u b l a m e a p
a l b l a z e t b o
m t r n d e c k l c
s h a k e t r e e k
k f v m p b e n d e
a l e s c a l e l t
t o l e n d r e c o
e c s t a k e t e n
f k o e s h o c k a

Down

1.   3.   5.
2.   4.   6.

V. Finding Words. The words in the spelling list appear in the beginning (A-H), middle (I-Q), or end (R-Z) of the **Glossary/SPELLEX®**. Write each word.

Beginning A-H	Middle I-Q	End R-Z
1. _____	1. _____	1. _____
2. _____	2. _____	2. _____
3. _____	3. _____	3. _____
4. _____		4. _____
5. _____		5. _____
6. _____		
7. _____		
8. _____		

Spelling Words

blade   blame   blaze   brave   shake   stake   skate   scale
lend   bend   melt   deck   flock   shock   blocks   pocket

VI. Sort Your Words.

a. In alphabetical order, write the eight words ending with a silent *e*.

1. _____   4. _____   7. _____

2. _____   5. _____   8. _____

3. _____   6. _____

b. What does the silent *e* do to the vowel *a* in each word?

c. Write the five words with *ck*.

1. _____   3. _____   5. _____

2. _____   4. _____

d. Write the three spelling words you have not used. Circle the final *lt* or *nd* in each word.

1. _____   2. _____   3. _____

21

VII. Solve the Puzzle. Solve the puzzle by using spelling words and one **Other Word Form** (p. 19).* Check your answers in the **Glossary/SPELLEX**®.

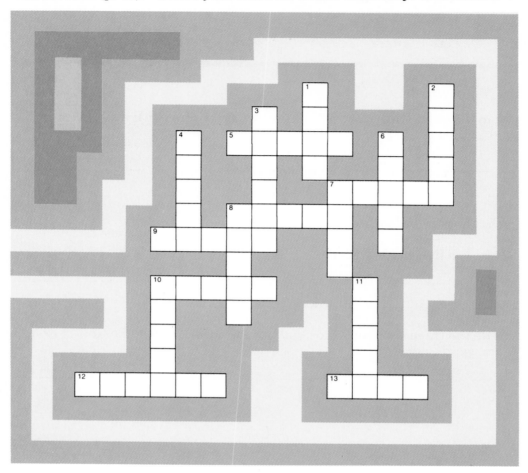

Across

5. a group of sheep
7. a bright flame
8. to perform on ice
9. what snow does, sooner or later*
10. done with the right hand
12. holds coins and handkerchiefs
13. opposite of *borrow*

Down

1. a set of playing cards
2. to find fault
3. solid pieces of wood
4. not afraid
6. a part of a knife
7. a curve in the road
8. used to hold up a tent
10. a sudden surprise
11. found on fish

VIII. Final Test. Write each spelling word.

1	2	3	4	5
alike	blade	history	mile	sum
arithmetic	brave	hunter	pocket	swift
began	crossing	knee	seemed	tore
being	fate	knife	shake	woke

I. Break the Code. Use the code to write an other word form for each spelling word. Write each word.

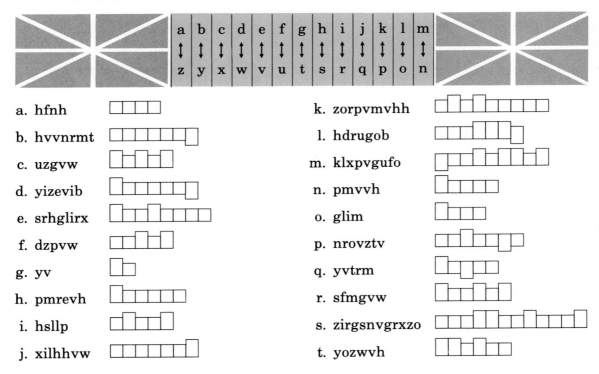

a. hfnh

b. hvvnrmt

c. uzgvw

d. yizevib

e. srhglirx

f. dzpvw

g. yv

h. pmrevh

i. hsllp

j. xilhhvw

k. zorpvmvhh

l. hdrugob

m. klxpvgufo

n. pmvvh

o. glim

p. nrovztv

q. yvtrm

r. sfmgvw

s. zirgsnvgrxzo

t. yozwvh

6

1	2	3	4	5
cape	dive	races	pile	holes
mapping	rack	ax	lump	enter
cases	saves	blaze	smile	slip
spin	bend	shine	flock	stake

II. Words in a Series. Use other word forms to complete each series. The number tells you in what column you can find the spelling word. Use each word or its other word form only once.

a. jackets, coats, (1) _____

b. heaps, loads, (4) _____

c. leaps, jumps, (2) _____

d. running, dashing, (3) _____

e. bars, poles, (2) _____

f. opening, pit, (5) _____

g. plan, chart, (1) _____

h. tools, hatchets, (3) _____

i. bumps, chunks, (4) _____

j. came in, walked in, (5) _____

k. kept, stored, (2) _____

l. box, crate, (1) _____

m. fell, tripped, (5) _____

n. grinning, laughing, (4) _____

o. burning, flaming, (3) _____

p. turning, circling, (1) _____

q. curved, twisted, (2) _____

r. herds, packs, (4) _____

s. glowing, glaring, (3) _____

t. pegs, sticks, (5) _____

24

1	2	3	4	5	
she's	size	he's	meet	won't	**6**
didn't	plum	prize	shock	slide	
backward	melt	can't	across	lace	
skate	knows	it's	grip	blame	

III. Sentence Completion. Write other word forms or the spelling words to complete the sentences. The number tells you in what column you can find the spelling word. Write each word or its other word form only once. If you need help, use the **Glossary/SPELLEX®**.

a. We (5) _____ be able to have a class (4) _____ before the field trip.

b. Sometimes (3) _____ not easy to (5) _____ my sneakers.

c. We (1) _____ buy many (2) _____ at the grocery store.

d. I think (1) _____ wearing shoes that are two (2) _____ too big for her.

e. Are you sure (3) _____ going to walk (4) _____ the old bridge?

f. We (3) _____ run (1) _____ without falling down.

g. I (2) _____ I can win one of the (3) _____ at the fair.

h. We (4) _____ the sides of the sled as we went (5) _____ down the hill.

i. They couldn't go (1) _____ because the ice on the pond had (2) _____ .

j. I was (4) _____ when my cousin (5) _____ me for eating all the cookies.

25

6

1	2	3	4	5
fade	madly	begun	knew	deck
dare	draft	lung	slid	scale
hire	camel	itself	knot	lend
wade	wore	begin	prices	blocks

IV. Calendar of Events. Use other word forms or the spelling words to write a silly or serious note for each day of a school calendar. Circle the other word forms and the spelling words you used. Two days are filled out for you.

MON	TUES	WED	THURS	FRI
1	2	3	4 *must* (*begin*) *report on* *giraffes*	5
8	9	10	11	12
15	16 *We will ride* *on* (*camels*) .	17	18	19
22	23	24	25	26

Lesson 7

I. Check Test. Write each spelling word.

II. Spelling Words and Phrases

drag	will **drag** it behind them
snap	to **snap** the pencil
trap	a harmless **trap**
scrap	**scrap** of cloth
bump	ran over a **bump**
club	**club** meeting
scrub	to **scrub** the floor
hung	**hung** in the closet
hungry	felt so **hungry**
hundred	a **hundred** or more
trust	honesty and **trust**
brush	will **brush** their teeth
bruise	a **bruise** on my elbow
stocking	in their **stocking** feet
unlock	to **unlock** the door
o'clock	almost three **o'clock**

III. Find a Fit. Write each word in its correct shape.

a.

b.

c.

d.

e.

f.

g.

h.

i.

j.

k.

l.

m.

n.

o.

p.

Other Word Forms

drags, dragged, dragging, snaps, snapped, snapping, traps, trapped, trapping, scraps, bumps, bumped, bumping, clubs, scrubs, scrubbed, scrubbing, hang, hangs, hanged, hanging, hunger, hungrier, hungriest, hundreds, trusts, trusted, trusting, brushes, brushed, brushing, bruises, bruised, bruising, stockings, unlocks, unlocked, unlocking

27

IV. Hide and Seek.
The spelling words and some **Other Word Forms** (p. 27) can be found in the word puzzle. The words appear across and down. Circle and write the words.

Spelling Words

Across

1. [   ]
2. [   ]
3. [   ]
4. [   ]
5. [   ]
6. [   ]

Down

1. [   ]
2. [   ]
3. [   ]
4. [   ]
5. [   ]
6. [   ]
7. [   ]
8. [   ]
9. [   ]
10. [   ]

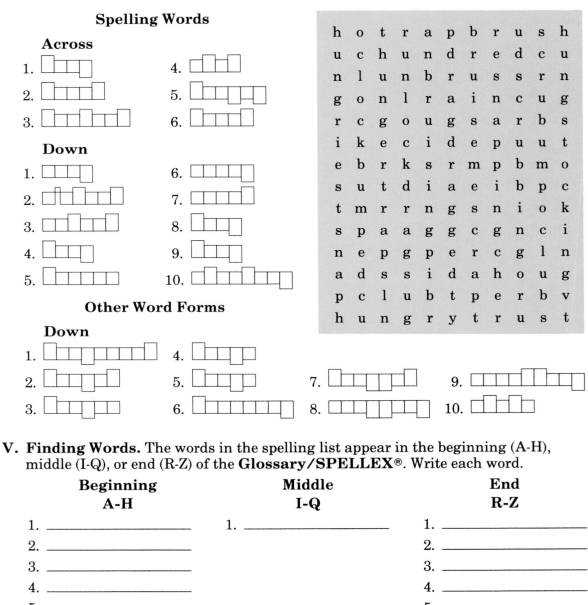

```
h o t r a p b r u s h
u c h u n d r e d c u
n l u n b r u s s r n
g o n l r a i n c u g
r c g o u g s a r b s
i k e c i d e p u u t
e b r k s r m p b m o
s u t d i a e i b p c
t m r r n g s n i o k
s p a a g g c g n c i
n e p g p e r c l n
a d s s i d a h o u g
p c l u b t p e r b v
h u n g r y t r u s t
```

Other Word Forms

Down

1. [   ]
2. [   ]
3. [   ]
4. [   ]
5. [   ]
6. [   ]
7. [   ]
8. [   ]
9. [   ]
10. [   ]

V. Finding Words.
The words in the spelling list appear in the beginning (A-H), middle (I-Q), or end (R-Z) of the **Glossary/SPELLEX®**. Write each word.

Beginning A-H	Middle I-Q	End R-Z
1. _____	1. _____	1. _____
2. _____		2. _____
3. _____		3. _____
4. _____		4. _____
5. _____		5. _____
6. _____		6. _____
7. _____		7. _____
8. _____		

28

Spelling Words

drag snap trap scrap bump club scrub hung hungry hundred trust brush bruise stocking unlock o'clock

VI. Little Word—Big Word. Write the spelling word that hides the answer to each clue. Then circle the little word that you find in each spelling word.

Example: This word hides a fast action. _____ b (rush)

a. This word hides the color of cherries. _____

b. This word hides a short sleep. _____

c. This word hides an old cloth. _____

d. This word hides the ruler of a country. _____

e. This word hides a reddish-brown color. _____

f. These two words hide a tool or instrument that is used with a key. _____ _____

g. These two words hide a knock on the door. _____ _____

VII. Three in a Row. Write a spelling word in the group it best fits.

a. black-and-blue, sore, _____

b. empty, wanting food, _____

c. attached, fastened, _____

d. racket, bat, _____

e. rub, wash, _____

f. lump, swelling, _____

g. paint, sweep, _____

VIII. Sort Your Words. Each spelling word has two or more consonants together. Write each spelling word. A word may go in more than one column.

Beginning Consonants Together	Middle Consonants Together	End Consonants Together
1. _____	1. _____	1. _____
2. _____	2. _____	2. _____
3. _____	3. _____	3. _____
4. _____	4. _____	4. _____
5. _____	5. _____	5. _____
6. _____		6. _____
7. _____		7. _____
8. _____		
9. _____		
10. _____		

Write the words that fit in no more than two columns. _____

_____ _____ _____

Write the word that fits in all three columns. _____

IX. Final Test. Write each spelling word.

Lesson 8

I. Check Test. Write each spelling word.

II. Spelling Words and Phrases

trim	a beard to **trim**
whip	crack of the **whip**
quit	will never **quit**
quite	not **quite** ready
tribe	peaceful **tribe**
pride	full of **pride**
crime	solved the **crime**
strike	to **strike** out
kept	**kept** apart
slept	**slept** soundly
fresh	**fresh** fish for sale
check	cashed a **check**
shell	**shell** on the beach
spend	to **spend** money
press	printing **press**
yellow	**yellow** ribbon

III. Find a Fit. Write each word in its correct shape.

a. ⬚⬚⬚⬛⬚

b. ⬚⬚⬚⬛⬚

c. ⬚⬛⬚⬚⬛⬚

d. ⬚⬚⬚⬛⬚

e. ⬚⬛⬚⬛

f. ⬚⬚⬚⬚⬚

g. ⬚⬚⬛⬚

h. ⬚⬚⬚⬚⬚

i. ⬚⬚⬚⬚⬛⬚

j. ⬚⬚⬚⬚⬚

k. ⬚⬚⬚⬚

l. ⬚⬚⬛⬚

m. ⬚⬚⬛

n. ⬚⬚⬚⬚

o. ⬚⬚⬚⬛⬚

p. ⬚⬚⬚⬛

Other Word Forms

trims, trimmed, trimming, whips, whipped, whipping, quits, quitting, quitter, tribes, tribal, prides, prideful, crimes, criminal, strikes, striking, struck, keep, keeps, keeping, keeper, sleep, sleeps, sleeping, sleepy, sleepier, sleepiest, freshly, fresher, freshest, checks, checked, checking, shells, shelled, shelling, spends, spending, spent, spender, presses, pressed, pressing, yellows, yellowed

IV. Missing Vowels. Find the missing vowels and write the spelling words.

a. pr __ d __   _____

b. q __ __ t __   _____

c. k __ pt   _____

d. sh __ ll   _____

e. y __ ll __ w   _____

f. tr __ m   _____

g. fr __ sh   _____

h. pr __ ss   _____

i. wh __ p   _____

j. cr __ m __   _____

k. q __ __ t   _____

l. ch __ ck   _____

m. sp __ nd   _____

n. tr __ b __   _____

o. sl __ pt   _____

p. str __ k __   _____

V. Scrambled Words. Unscramble the scrambled word to find the spelling word that completes the sentence. Write the word.

Scrambled Words

a. We will _____ working at five.   tuiq

b. Buy some _____ milk for dinner.   shefr

c. Don't _____ too much time in the sun.   ndesp

d. She _____ comfortably on the couch.   ptsle

e. Don't try to _____ the baseball too hard.   ikestr

f. The _____ was committed at midnight.   meicr

g. Use these clippers to _____ the hedge.   mitr

h. Some animal once lived in this _____ .   lelsh

i. _____ the strips of wood together.   sespr

j. He learned the language of the _____ .   ebitr

k. She has always _____ this lucky coin.   ptek

l. We were _____ pleased to hear the good news.   teqiu

m. Use blue paint and _____ paint to make green.   lleyow

n. Write your name on the _____ .   eckch

o. _____ is the result of a job well done.   dipre

p. Use this spoon to _____ the cake batter.   piwh

Spelling Words

trim   whip   quit   quite   tribe   pride   crime   strike
kept   slept   fresh   check   shell   spend   press   yellow

VI. Words and Meanings. Write a spelling word for each meaning. Check your
answers in the **Glossary/SPELLEX®**.

a. a bank order to pay money _____

b. a strap attached to a handle _____

c. to put force on something _____

d. to make neat by cutting _____

e. to give up _____

f. an unlawful action _____

g. to hit _____

h. rested _____

i. had for a long time _____

j. to pay out money _____

k. just made _____

l. a group of people _____

m. a hard covering on some animals _____

n. pleasure in one's actions _____

o. a color _____

p. completely _____

VII. All in a Sentence. Use each of the spelling words or **Other Word Forms** (p. 31) in sentences about a faraway island in the Pacific Ocean. Circle the spelling words and the other word forms you used.

The Pacific Isle

Example: *We collected* (*yellow*) (*shells*) .

VIII. Final Test. Write each spelling word.

Lesson 9

I. Check Test. Write each spelling word.

II. Spelling Words and Phrases

sail	lowered the **sail**
jail	was put in **jail**
nails	hammered the **nails**
wait	if you **wait**
pain	**pain** in my neck
again	phoned once **again**
swim	learned to **swim**
thick	**thick** and thin
brick	the **brick** wall
trick	a magic **trick**
drill	the sound of the **drill**
skill	learned a new **skill**
loud	a long, **loud** cheer
proud	felt very **proud**
shout	a **shout** of joy
outfits	new camping **outfits**

III. Find a Fit. Write each word in its correct shape.

a. ☐☐☐☐

b. ☐☐☐☐☐

c. ☐☐☐☐

d. ☐☐☐☐☐

e. ☐☐☐☐☐

f. ☐☐☐☐☐☐☐

g. ☐☐☐☐☐

h. ☐☐☐☐☐

i. ☐☐☐☐☐

j. ☐☐☐☐

k. ☐☐☐☐☐

l. ☐☐☐☐

m. ☐☐☐☐

n. ☐☐☐☐☐

o. ☐☐☐☐

p. ☐☐☐☐☐

Other Word Forms
sails, sailed, sailing, sailor, jails, jailed, jailer, nail, nailed, nailing, waits, waited, waiting, waiter, pains, painful, swims, swam, swimming, thicker, thickest, thickly, bricks, tricks, tricky, trickier, trickiest, drills, drilled, drilling, skills, skillful, skillfully, skilled, louder, loudest, loudly, proudly, prouder, proudest, shouts, shouted, shouting, outfit, outfitted, outfitting

IV. Sort Your Words.

a. Write the spelling words in groups that rhyme.

1. _____   1. _____

2. _____   2. _____

1. _____   1. _____

2. _____   2. _____

3. _____

b. Write the spelling words that did not fit into a rhyming group.

1. _____   5. _____

2. _____   6. _____

3. _____   7. _____

4. _____

c. Put a check beside the compound word.

V. Word Search. The spelling words can be found in the word puzzle. The words appear across and down. Circle and write the words.

Across

1. ⬜⬜⬜⬜
2. ⬜⬜⬜⬜
3. ⬜⬜⬜⬜⬜
4. ⬜⬜⬜⬜⬜⬜
5. ⬜⬜⬜⬜⬜
6. ⬜⬜⬜⬜
7. ⬜⬜⬜⬜
8. ⬜⬜⬜⬜⬜

s	a	i	l	b	p	a	i	n
h	e	s	p	r	o	u	d	o
o	u	t	f	i	t	s	w	e
u	n	r	o	c	d	k	a	t
t	h	i	c	k	r	i	i	s
a	l	c	m	s	i	l	t	s
g	o	k	s	w	l	l	m	n
a	s	j	a	i	l	o	u	d
i	n	t	o	m	e	t	s	y
n	a	i	l	s	t	p	o	e

Down

1. ⬜⬜⬜⬜⬜   3. ⬜⬜⬜⬜⬜   5. ⬜⬜⬜⬜   7. ⬜⬜⬜⬜⬜

2. ⬜⬜⬜⬜⬜   4. ⬜⬜⬜⬜⬜   6. ⬜⬜⬜⬜⬜   8. ⬜⬜⬜⬜

Spelling Words

sail jail nails wait pain again swim thick
brick trick drill skill loud proud shout outfits

VI. Words and Meanings. Write a spelling word for each meaning. Check your answers in the **Glossary/SPELLEX®**.

a. pointed metal pieces that hold things together _____

b. material that catches wind on a boat _____

c. to move in water with arms and legs _____

d. a place where lawbreakers are kept _____

e. the ability to do something well _____

f. a tool for making holes _____

g. a block of baked clay _____

h. feeling very pleased _____

i. to stay in a place _____

j. sets of equipment _____

k. one more time _____

l. a clever act _____

m. a loud cry _____

n. not quiet _____

o. not thin _____

p. hurt _____

VII. Homophones. Homophones are words with the same sound. Write the homophone for each word.

a. sale   _____

b. weight   _____

c. pane   _____

VIII. Write Your Journal. Use each of the spelling words or **Other Word Forms** (p. 35) to write a page in your journal about the day you helped your class clean the playground. Circle the spelling words and the other word forms you used.

IX. Final Test. Write each spelling word.

Lesson 10

I. Check Test. Write each spelling word.

II. Spelling Words and Phrases

chase	a dangerous **chase**
space	far into **space**
trace	a **trace** of smoke
scrape	to **scrape** the plate
frame	the picture **frame**
shame	a **shame** to miss the parade
share	a **share** of the dessert
gown	white wedding **gown**
clown	a **clown** with big feet
power	**power** tools
tower	tall steel **tower**
shower	cold **shower**
crowd	a **crowd** at the game
homesick	**homesick** camper
notebooks	**notebooks** for school
sore	**sore** toe

III. Find a Fit. Write each word in its correct shape.

a.
b.
c.
d.
e.
f.
g.
h.
i.
j.
k.
l.
m.
n.
o.
p.

Other Word Forms

chases, chased, chasing, spaces, spaced, spacing, traces, traced, tracing, scrapes, scraped, scraping, frames, shames, shameful, shamed, shaming, shares, shared, sharing, gowns, clowns, clowning, powers, powerful, towers, towered, towering, showers, showered, showering, crowds, crowded, homesickness, notebook, sorely, sorer, sorest

IV. Finding Words. The words in the spelling list appear in the beginning (A-H), middle (I-Q), or end (R-Z) of the **Glossary/SPELLEX®**. Write each word.

Beginning A-H	Middle I-Q	End R-Z
1. _____	1. _____	1. _____
2. _____	2. _____	2. _____
3. _____		3. _____
4. _____		4. _____
5. _____		5. _____
6. _____		6. _____
		7. _____
		8. _____

V. Sort Your Words.

a. Write each spelling word. Beside each word write an **Other Word Form** (p. 39).

Words With *ow*	Other Word Forms		Words With a Long *a*	Other Word Forms
1. _____	_____		1. _____	_____
2. _____	_____		2. _____	_____
3. _____	_____		3. _____	_____
4. _____	_____		4. _____	_____
5. _____	_____		5. _____	_____
6. _____	_____		6. _____	_____

Words With *sh*	Other Word Forms		Words With a Long *o*	Other Word Forms
1. _____	_____		1. _____	_____
2. _____	_____		2. _____	_____
3. _____	_____			

b. Write the two words that fit in more than one box. _____ _____

c. Write the word that does not fit in any of the boxes. _____

Spelling Words

chase   space   trace   scrape   frame   shame   share   gown
clown   power   tower   shower   crowd   homesick   notebooks   sore

VI. **Name the Book.** Solve the puzzles. Then read down one column to find the title of a famous storybook.

a. what a _____   __ __ __ ☐ __

b. painful   __ ☐ __ __

c. to draw over   ☐ __ __ __ __

d. to divide into parts   __ ☐ __ __ __

e. rain   __ __ __ __ ☐

f. a picture _____   __ ☐ __ __

g. dress   ☐ __ __ __

h. lots of people   __ __ ☐ __ __

i. a tall, slender building   __ ☐ __ __ __

j. to rub off   ☐ __ __ __ __ __

k. to run after   __ __ __ __ ☐

l. school supplies   __ __ ☐ __ __ __ __ __

m. an open area   __ __ ☐ __ __

n. a joker   __ ☐ __ __ __

o. strength   __ __ ☐ __ __

p. missing one's home   __ __ __ __ ☐ __ __

The famous story book is: _____   _____   _____

41

VII. Writing Sentences. Write each set of words in a sentence. You may use **Other Word Forms** (p. 39).

1. homesick—crowd

2. scrape—sore

3. notebooks—share

4. shower—power

5. tower—space

6. shame—clown

7. frame—trace

8. chase—gown

VIII. Final Test. Write each spelling word.

Lesson 11

I. Check Test. Write each spelling word.

II. Spelling Words and Phrases

mild	**mild** weather
bind	to **bind** the book
blind	a **blind** corner
climb	whenever they **climb**
higher	the **higher** of the two flags
highest	the **highest** mountain
highway	the longest **highway**
mighty	a **mighty** roar
post	fence **post**
mostly	**mostly** in the morning
almost	**almost** there
sort	some **sort** of game
sword	a dull, broad **sword**
worn	**worn** only in winter
worth	our money's **worth**
worry	nothing to **worry** about

III. Find a Fit. Write each word in its correct shape.

a. ☐☐☐☐

b. ☐☐☐☐

c. ☐☐☐☐

d. ☐☐☐☐☐

e. ☐☐☐☐☐

f. ☐☐☐☐

g. ☐☐☐☐☐

h. ☐☐☐☐☐☐

i. ☐☐☐☐☐

j. ☐☐☐☐☐

k. ☐☐☐☐

l. ☐☐☐☐

m. ☐☐☐☐☐☐

n. ☐☐☐☐☐

o. ☐☐☐☐☐

p. ☐☐☐☐☐☐

Other Word Forms

milder, mildest, mildly, binds, binder, binding, bound, blinds, blinded, blinding, blindly, climbs, climbed, climbing, high, highly, highways, might, mightier, mightiest, posts, posted, posting, much, more, most, sorts, sorted, sorting, swords, wear, wore, wearing, worthless, worthy, worries, worried, worrying

All in a Row. Write the sixteen spelling words in alphabetical order. Then join the boxed letters and write four hidden words.

1. _ _ ☐ _ _ _

2. _ ☐ _ _ _

3. _ ☐ _ _ _ _

4. _ ☐ _ _ _ _

Hidden Word: _____

9. _ _ ☐ _

10. _ ☐ _ _ _ _

11. _ _ ☐ _

12. _ _ _ ☐

Hidden Word: _____

5. _ _ _ ☐ _ _

6. _ ☐ _ _ _ _

7. _ _ ☐ _ _ _ _

8. _ _ _ ☐ _ _

Hidden Word: _____

13. _ _ _ _ ☐

14. _ ☐ _ _

15. _ ☐ _ _ _

16. _ _ ☐ _ _

Hidden Word: _____

V. Base Words. The spelling list contains eleven base words and five words that are not base words. Write each spelling word.

Words That Are Not Base Words	Base Words	Words That Are Not Base Words	Base Words
a. worthy	_____	i. blindly	_____
b. worrying	_____	j. sorting	_____
c. highways	_____	k. _____	high
d. mildly	_____	l. _____	high
e. swords	_____	m. _____	might
f. posted	_____	n. _____	wear
g. binder	_____	o. _____	much
h. climbing	_____		

Write the one base word not used above. _____

Spelling Words

*mild bind blind climb higher highest highway mighty
post mostly almost sort sword worn worth worry*

VI. Three in a Row. Write a spelling word in the group it best fits.

a. feel troubled, be uneasy, ———————————

b. hidden, not seeing, ———————————

c. nearly, close to, ———————————

d. not hot, not cold, ———————————

e. value, importance, ———————————

f. kind, type, ———————————

g. ragged, damaged, ———————————

h. tie together, glue, ———————————

i. wood marker, fence holder, ———————————

j. mainly, for the most part, ———————————

VII. Seen but Not Heard. Write the six spelling words that have silent consonants.

a. _____   c. _____   e. _____

b. _____   d. _____   f. _____

VIII. All in a Sentence. Use each of the spelling words or **Other Word Forms** (p. 43) in sentences about your favorite pet or a sport you like. Circle the spelling words and the other word forms you used.

<u>My Favorite Pet</u> or <u>My Favorite Sport</u>

Example: *My cat* (*climbs*) *upon the shelf.*

IX. Final Test. Write each spelling word.

1	**2**	**3**	**4**	**5**
bruise	hung	outfits	proud	thick
crime	hungry	pain	quit	unlock
higher	kept	power	shame	worry
homesick	mighty	pride	sore	worth

I. Hide and Seek. Twenty other word forms can be found in the word puzzle. The words appear across and down. Circle and write each word. If you need help, use the **Glossary/SPELLEX®**.

Across

1.
2.
3.
4.
5.
6.
7.
8.
9.

```
t  h  i  c  k  e  r  b  s  h  a  m  e  d  q
h  u  n  g  r  i  e  r  x  s  o  r  e  l  y
a  m  p  a  i  n  f  u  l  n  e  u  t  z  s
n  c  f  k  l  r  q  i  n  h  g  n  p  v  w
g  k  e  e  p  t  u  s  o  a  b  l  e  h  o
w  i  z  a  o  r  i  e  p  p  o  o  s  l  r
h  b  c  d  w  f  t  d  r  r  i  c  p  a  r
c  t  h  g  e  s  s  u  i  o  r  k  c  d  i
r  w  j  o  r  e  f  w  d  u  b  e  h  o  e
i  o  u  t  f  i  t  z  e  d  o  d  i  t  d
m  r  v  n  u  l  d  o  s  l  y  v  g  r  e
i  t  a  b  l  c  h  k  p  y  s  c  h  w  a
n  h  z  h  o  m  e  s  i  c  k  n  e  s  s
a  y  e  r  u  k  n  t  b  m  o  v  s  i  r
l  m  i  g  h  t  i  e  r  u  e  j  t  l  n
```

Down

1.
2.
3.
4.
5.
6.
7.
8.

9.   10.   11.

47

12

1	2	3	4	5
trap	tribe	trick	scrape	sort
trust	trim	sail	gown	post
hundred	press	jail	crowd	brick
brush	check	drill	tower	blind

II. Word Operations. Use words from the spelling list to complete the exercises below. If you need help, use the **Glossary/SPELLEX®**.

a. **Operation Past Tense.** Write the *ed* form of each word.

1. trust   *trusted*
2. blind
3. post
4. tower
5. press
6. check
7. trick
8. crowd
9. drill
10. brush

b. **Operation Plural.** Write the *s* form of each word.

1. sort
2. hundred
3. trim
4. jail
5. gown
6. scrape
7. brick
8. sail
9. trap
10. tribe

1	2	3	4	5
bind	club	nails	shower	swim
chase	drag	scrub	slept	sword
climb	highest	share	snap	wait
clown	highway	shell	strike	whip

III. Word Clues. Write the spelling word that goes with each word clue. The number after each clue tells you in what column you can find the spelling word. Then write an other word form for each spelling word. If you need help, use the **Glossary/SPELLEX®**.

Word Clue	**Spelling Word**	**Other Word Form**
a. to make a sharp sound (4)	___ ___ ___ ___	_____
b. to rub clean (3)	___ ___ ___ ___ ___	_____
c. to pull along slowly (2)	___ ___ ___ ___	_____
d. a group of people who meet (2)	___ ___ ___ ___	_____
e. a hard outer covering (3)	___ ___ ___ ___ ___	_____
f. to hit (4)	___ ___ ___ ___ ___ ___	_____
g. a strap on a handle (5)	___ ___ ___ ___	_____
h. rested (4)	___ ___ ___ ___ ___	_____
i. pointed pieces of metal (3)	___ ___ ___ ___ ___	_____
j. to move in water (5)	___ ___ ___ ___	_____
k. to tie together (1)	___ ___ ___ ___	_____
l. to stay in a place (5)	___ ___ ___ ___	_____
m. a funny circus person (1)	___ ___ ___ ___ ___	_____
n. a bath of spraying water (4)	___ ___ ___ ___ ___ ___	_____
o. to use with others (3)	___ ___ ___ ___ ___	_____
p. a sharp weapon (5)	___ ___ ___ ___ ___	_____
q. to move upward (1)	___ ___ ___ ___ ___	_____
r. tallest (2)	___ ___ ___ ___ ___ ___ ___	_____
s. a main road (2)	___ ___ ___ ___ ___ ___ ___	_____
t. to run after (1)	___ ___ ___ ___ ___	_____

12

1	2	3	4	5
bump	spend	shout	notebooks	mostly
o'clock	quite	loud	frame	almost
stocking	fresh	skill	trace	mild
scrap	yellow	again	space	worn

IV. Sentences in Paragraphs. Write other word forms or the spelling words to complete the sentences. Use the words from column 1 to complete paragraph 1, and so on. Write each word or its other word form only once. If you need help, use the **Glossary/SPELLEX®**.

1. At one __ __ __ __ __ __ in the morning, I crept downstairs in my

    __ __ __ __ __ __ __ __ feet to the refrigerator. Quietly, I opened the

    door to see if any __ __ __ __ __ __ of food were there. While reaching for

    the cheese, I __ __ __ __ __ __ my head and wished I had stayed in bed.

2. In the garden shop, we saw lovely __ __ __ __ __ __ flowers that had

    been __ __ __ __ __ __ __ cut. They were __ __ __ __ __

    beautiful, but we couldn't buy any because we had __ __ __ __ __ all of

    our money at the movies.

3. Once __ __ __ __ __ our voices got __ __ __ __ __ __ as we

    __ __ __ __ __ __ __ and laughed during the math game. Our teacher

    was pleased to see us using the new __ __ __ __ __ __ we had learned.

4. I wanted to make a picture __ __ __ __ __ for a drawing I had

    __ __ __ __ __ __ in my art __ __ __ __ __ __ __ __ . I had

    no wood for a real frame. I cut some blue paper and __ __ __ __ __ __ it

    evenly around my drawing to make a border.

5. It is __ __ __ __ __ __ spring, and the __ __ __ __ __ __

    weather is coming. I have to __ __ __ __ a coat __ __ __ __ often in

    the morning when I walk to school.

Lesson 13

I. Check Test. Write each spelling word.

II. Spelling Words and Phrases

bid	will **bid** at the auction
dim	to **dim** the lights
tin	made of **tin**
mix	to **mix** and pour
sixth	**sixth** time
sixteen	**sixteen** steps to the door
mint	flavor of **mint**
mist	hidden in the **mist**
ticket	movie **ticket**
chart	a temperature **chart**
March	a windy **March**
marble	**marble** floors
marker	a red **marker**
farther	**farther** away
reward	collected the **reward**
plane	taking a **plane**
replace	will **replace** the book
skating	**skating** party

III. Find a Fit. Write each word in its correct shape.

a.
b.
c.
d.
e.
f.
g.
h.
i.
j.
k.
l.
m.
n.
o.
p.
q.
r.

Other Word Forms

bids, bidding, bidder, dims, dimmed, dimming, dimmer, dimmest, dimly, tins, tinned, mixes, mixed, mixing, mixer, six, sixths, sixteenth, mints, minted, minting, mists, misted, misting, misty, tickets, ticketed, ticketing, charts, charted, charting, Mar., marbles, marbled, marbling, mark, marks, marked, marking, far, farthest, rewards, rewarded, rewarding, planes, replaces, replaced, replacing, skate, skated, skater

IV. Word Match-ups.
Find a word in the spelling list that best fits each phrase. Check your answers in the **Glossary/SPELLEX®.**

a. a winter sport _____

b. to stir together _____

c. flies in the air _____

d. the third month _____

e. twelve plus four _____

f. a crayon _____

g. light rain _____

h. a flavorful plant _____

i. before the seventh _____

j. not nearer _____

k. to make an offer _____

l. a round glass toy _____

m. to make darker _____

n. to fill the place of _____

o. metal for cans _____

p. a movie pass _____

q. a prize _____

r. a map _____

V. All in a Row.
Write the eighteen spelling words in alphabetical order. Then join the boxed letters and write four hidden words.

1. ☐ __ __

2. __ __ ☐ __ __

3. __ ☐ __

4. __ __ __ ☐ __ __ __

Hidden Word: _____

5. __ __ __ ☐ __ __

6. __ ☐ __ __ __

7. __ __ ☐ __ __ __

8. __ __ ☐ __ __

9. __ __ ☐ __

Hidden Word: _____

10. ☐ __ __

11. __ __ ☐ __ __

12. __ __ __ ☐ __ __ __

13. __ ☐ __ __ __ __

Hidden Word: _____

14. ☐ __ __ __ __ __

15. __ __ __ ☐ __

16. __ __ ☐ __ __ __ __

17. __ ☐ __ __ __ __

18. __ __ ☐ __

Hidden Word: _____

52

Spelling Words

bid   dim   tin   mix   sixth   sixteen   mint   mist ticket   chart   March   marble   marker   farther reward   plane   replace   skating

VI. Solve the Puzzle. Solve the puzzle by using words from the spelling list. Check your answers in the **Glossary/SPELLEX®**.

Across

3. money given for information
7. after the fifth
8. something that holds your place
9. a round plaything
11. to offer to pay a certain price
12. a tag or label
13. to stir
14. a plant used for flavoring

Down

1. aircraft
2. a graph or map
3. to take the place of
4. not bright
5. at a greater distance
6. a month
7. gliding on ice
10. eight plus eight
12. a silvery metal
13. a bath of spraying water

VII. Writing Sentences. Write each set of words in a sentence. You may use **Other Word Forms** (p. 51).

1. bid—ticket

2. plane—mist

3. mix—mint

4. sixth—March

5. marble—reward

6. replace—tin

7. marker—chart

8. farther—sixteen

9. skating—dim

VIII. Final Test. Write each spelling word.

I. Check Test. Write each spelling word.

II. Spelling Words and Phrases

oil	motor **oil**
boil	will **boil** the water
soil	dark, wet **soil**
join	if they **join** us
coin	flipped a **coin**
noise	a sudden **noise**
point	**point** of the story
sliced	**sliced** tomatoes
sliding	a **sliding** door
driving	**driving** carefully
shining	**shining** the floor
writer	sky **writer**
river	a winding **river**
deliver	a load to **deliver**
silver	**silver** and gold
women	several **women**
Wednesday	next **Wednesday**
September	the first of **September**

III. Find a Fit. Write each word in its correct shape.

a. ☐☐☐☐☐
b. ☐☐☐☐☐
c. ☐☐☐☐☐
d. ☐☐☐☐☐☐☐
e. ☐☐
f. ☐☐☐☐☐
g. ☐☐☐☐
h. ☐☐☐☐☐☐
i. ☐☐☐☐☐☐
j. ☐☐☐☐
k. ☐☐☐☐
l. ☐☐☐☐☐☐
m. ☐☐☐☐
n. ☐☐☐☐☐☐
o. ☐☐☐☐☐☐☐
p. ☐☐☐☐☐
q. ☐☐☐☐☐
r. ☐☐☐☐☐☐

Other Word Forms

oils, oiled, oiling, oily, boils, boiled, boiling, boiler, soils, soiled, soiling, joins, joined, joining, coins, coined, coining, noisy, noisier, noisiest, noisily, points, pointed, pointing, pointer, slice, slices, slicing, slicer, slide, slid, slider, drive, drives, drove, shine, shines, shone, shined, shiny, write, writes, wrote, writing, written, rivers, delivers, delivered, delivering, delivery, silvery, woman, womanly, Wed., Sept.

IV. Sort Your Words. Write the spelling words in the correct columns. Check your answers in the **Glossary/SPELLEX®**. You will have two words left over.

Words With a Short *i* Sound	Words With a Long *i* Sound	Words With an *oi* Sound
1. _____	1. _____	1. _____
2. _____	2. _____	2. _____
3. _____	3. _____	3. _____
4. _____	4. _____	4. _____
	5. _____	5. _____
		6. _____
		7. _____

Leftover words: _____   _____

V. Word Operations. As a word doctor, you must change some words before adding a suffix. Make the changes that are needed and write the new words. Some words will not need a change.

Word	Suffix	New Word
a. boil	er	_____
b. join	ing	_____
c. write	er	_____
d. deliver	ing	_____
e. slice	ed	_____
f. point	ed	_____
g. drive	ing	_____
h. soil	ed	_____
i. shine	ing	_____
j. oil	ing	_____
k. slide	ing	_____
l. coin	ed	_____

Spelling Words

oil boil soil join coin noise point sliced
sliding driving shining writer river deliver
silver women Wednesday September

VI. Word Swap. Use the spelling words and **Other Word Forms** (p. 55) to replace the underlined words or phrases. Write the words.

On the second (a.) <u>Tuesday</u> of (b.) <u>January</u>, six (c.) <u>men</u> stepped into the (d.) <u>sparkling</u> bus. The conductor (e.) <u>aimed</u> his fingers at a box and asked the people to put their (f.) <u>whitish</u> (g.) <u>dimes</u> into it. There was so much (h.) <u>loud sound</u> that the driver stopped (i.) <u>making the bus move</u>. The bus began (j.) <u>skidding</u> on a puddle of (k.) <u>slime</u> and just missed going into a (l.) <u>lake</u>. A (m.) <u>person who makes up stories</u> was on his way to (n.) <u>bring</u> his story to town. He (o.) <u>got together with</u> some people from the bus. One woman showed him the (p.) <u>dirt</u> they had landed in. Then she dropped her package of (q.) <u>cooked</u>, (r.) <u>carved</u> meat. The bus was soon towed.

a. _____ g. _____ m. _____

b. _____ h. _____ n. _____

c. _____ i. _____ o. _____

d. _____ j. _____ p. _____

e. _____ k. _____ q. _____

f. _____ l. _____ r. _____

VII. Be a Word Detective. The same two vowels are missing from each of the words below. Write the words.

a. s __ __ l   _____

b. b __ __ l   _____

c. p __ __ nt   _____

d. j __ __ n   _____

e. c __ __ n   _____

f. n __ __ se   _____

g. __ __ l   _____

VIII. Words and Meanings. Write a spelling word for each meaning. Check your answers in the **Glossary/SPELLEX®**.

a. to meet _____

b. cut into thin, flat pieces _____

c. dirt _____

d. to heat until bubbling _____

e. moving easily _____

f. a main idea _____

g. a metal piece of money _____

h. making bright _____

i. the ninth month of the year _____

j. an author _____

k. a day of the week _____

l. a greasy substance _____

m. adult female human beings _____

n. to carry and hand out _____

o. controlling the movement of a car _____

p. a natural stream of water _____

q. a loud sound _____

r. a shiny white metal _____

IX. Writing Sentences. Write each set of words in a sentence. You may use **Other Word Forms** (p. 55).

1. river—noise

2. women—Wednesday

3. September—silver

X. Final Test. Write each spelling word.

58

Lesson 15

I. Check Test. Write each spelling word.

II. Spelling Words and Phrases

dawn	just before **dawn**
lawn	a **lawn** mower
laws	passed new **laws**
draw	had to **draw** straws
straw	a bale of **straw**
lean	to **lean** against
meal	finished the **meal**
weak	a **weak** voice
fears	often **fears** danger
earn	whatever we **earn**
early	**early** the next day
earth	the rotation of the **earth**
heard	**heard** an echo
heart	a valentine **heart**
hammer	a **hammer** and a nail
matter	doesn't **matter**
madder	**madder** than ever
ladder	up the **ladder**

III. Find a Fit. Write each word in its correct shape.

a.

b.

c.

d.

e.

f.

g.

h.

i.

j.

k.

l.

m.

n.

o.

p.

q.

r.

Other Word Forms

dawns, dawned, dawning, lawns, law, lawful, lawyer, draws, drew, drawing, drawer, straws, leans, leaned, leaning, meals, weaker, weakest, weakly, fear, feared, fearing, fearful, earns, earned, earning, earlier, earliest, earthy, earthly, hear, hears, hearing, hearts, hearty, heartier, heartiest, hammers, hammered, hammering, matters, mad, maddest, madly, ladders

IV. Missing Vowels. Find the missing vowels and write the spelling words.

a. l __ __ n   _____

b. __ __ rl __   _____

c. d __ wn   _____

d. h __ mm __ r   _____

e. l __ dd __ r   _____

f. dr __ w   _____

g. m __ dd __ r   _____

h. m __ tt __ r   _____

i. h __ __ rd   _____

j. l __ wn   _____

k. __ __ rn   _____

l. h __ __ rt   _____

m. str __ w   _____

n. __ __ rth   _____

o. m __ __ l   _____

p. l __ ws   _____

q. w __ __ k   _____

r. f __ __ rs   _____

V. Base Words. The spelling list contains fourteen base words and four words that are not base words. Write each spelling word.

Words That Are Not Base Words	Base Words	Words That Are Not Base Words	Base Words
a. earning	_____	j. heartiest	_____
b. earliest	_____	k. straws	_____
c. meals	_____	l. leaning	_____
d. matters	_____	m. drew	_____
e. dawning	_____	n. earthly	_____
f. ladders	_____	o. _____	hear
g. weakly	_____	p. _____	mad
h. hammering	_____	q. _____	fear
i. lawns	_____	r. _____	law

Spelling Words

dawn   lawn   laws   draw   straw   lean   meal
weak   fears   earn   early   earth   heard   heart
hammer   matter   madder   ladder

VI. Rearrange and Change.
How fast can you rearrange the scrambled words to make all of the spelling words? Ask a partner to time you. You must write each word. Ready? Begin!

a.	b.	c.	d.	e.	f.
wnad	wadr	wastr	rthae	ealm	neal

g.	h.	i.	j.	k.	l.
redlad	arne	yearl	searf	keaw	awls

m.	n.	o.	p.	q.	r.
remham	tremat	harde	awnl	dremad	thear

Spelling Words

a. _____   g. _____   m. _____

b. _____   h. _____   n. _____

c. _____   i. _____   o. _____

d. _____   j. _____   p. _____

e. _____   k. _____   q. _____

f. _____   l. _____   r. _____

Record your time.   Minutes _____   Seconds _____

VII. All in a Sentence. Use each of the spelling words in sentences about one of the following titles. You may use **Other Word Forms** (p. 59). Circle the spelling words and the other word forms you used.

<u>Playing With a Balloon</u> or <u>Building a Hut</u>

Example: *In the* (*dawn*) *, balloons sailed over the front* (*lawn*) *.*

VIII. Final Test. Write each spelling word.

I. Check Test. Write each spelling word.

II. Spelling Words and Phrases

death	sudden **death**
breath	out of **breath**
ahead	far **ahead**
thread	needle and **thread**
already	**already** there
wear	will **wear** a coat
lightly	stepped **lightly**
lightning	flash of **lightning**
broke	**broke** in two
globe	the spinning **globe**
froze	**froze** solid
November	the end of **November**
score	the winning **score**
porch	under the **porch**
Tuesday	**Tuesday** afternoon
music	distant **music**
few	a **few** children
during	**during** the morning

III. Find a Fit. Write each word in its correct shape.

a.

b.

c.

d.

e.

f.

g.

h.

i.

j.

k.

l.

m.

n.

o.

p.

q.

r.

Other Word Forms

deaths, deathly, breaths, breathed, breathing, breathless, threads, threading, wears, wore, worn, wearing, light, lights, lit, lighting, lighter, lightest, break, breaks, breaking, broken, globes, global, freeze, freezes, frozen, freezing, Nov., scores, scoring, porches, Tues., musical, musically, musician, fewer, fewest

IV. Word Match-ups. Find a word in the spelling list that best fits each word or phrase below. Check your answers in the **Glossary/SPELLEX**®.

a. in front _____

b. the total of points in a game _____

c. a model of the earth _____

d. an autumn month _____

e. thin string _____

f. to have clothing on _____

g. screened-in room _____

h. notes and scales _____

i. a weekday _____

j. made cold and solid _____

k. at some point of time _____

l. not many _____

m. goes with thunder _____

n. air taken into the body _____

o. came apart _____

p. softly _____

q. the end of life _____

r. by this time _____

V. Word Clues. Be a detective. Study the clues to uncover the words from the spelling list. Write the words.

a. clef, note, staff, conductor, _____

b. dark, stormy, thunder, flash, _____

c. Thanksgiving, cold, football, month, _____

d. weekday, school, work, study, _____

e. chairs, front, house, outside, _____

f. team, goal, points, touchdown, _____

g. earth, round, equator, axis, _____

h. tailor, sew, needle, stitch, _____

i. gasp, inhale, air, oxygen, _____

Spelling Words

death   breath   ahead   thread   already   wear
lightly   lightning   broke   globe   froze   November
score   porch   Tuesday   music   few   during

VI. Guide Words. These word pairs are guide words from the **Glossary/SPELLEX®**. Write the words from the spelling list that appear on the same page as each pair of guide words.

Example:

huge—kept
_____ *hunter*
_____ *iron*

above—ax
1. _____
2. _____

blame—bucket
3. _____
4. _____

correct—dirt
5. _____

dirty—evening
6. _____

event—flock
7. _____

floor—gang
8. _____

get—hate
9. _____

leaf—lucky
10. _____
11. _____

mean—nineteen
12. _____

nobody—outfit
13. _____

pocket—purse
14. _____

scale—sheet
15. _____

stream—thread
16. _____

throw—unlock
17. _____

until—worry
18. _____

The Animals

VII. Word Opposites. Antonyms are word opposites. Find the antonym from the spelling list for each word or words below.

a. many _____

b. life _____

c. heavily _____

d. not yet _____

e. melted _____

f. behind _____

g. fixed _____

h. undress _____

i. before and after _____

VIII. Writing Sentences. Write each set of words in a sentence. You may use **Other Word Forms** (p. 63).

1. lightly—music

2. broke—globe

3. few—breath

4. wear—froze

5. lightning—ahead

6. death—already

7. score—during

8. Tuesday—November

9. thread—porch

IX. Final Test. Write each spelling word.

66

Lesson 17

I. Check Test. Write each spelling word.

II. Spelling Words and Phrases

until	**until** you come
study	tried to **study**
lucky	your **lucky** charm
bucket	the **bucket** of cement
number	remembered their **number**
Sunday	**Sunday** gathering
sir	**sir** or madam
shirt	checkered **shirt**
dirty	**dirty** clothes
birthday	my next **birthday**
leaf	a yellow **leaf**
leak	a **leak** in the hose
leading	**leading** the race
heating	**heating** the water
scold	to **scold** for nothing
oldest	**oldest** in the family
holding	**holding** tighter
poster	baseball **poster**

III. Find a Fit. Write each word in its correct shape.

a.
b.
c.
d.
e.
f.
g.
h.
i.
j.
k.
l.
m.
n.
o.
p.
q.
r.

Other Word Forms

studies, studied, studying, student, studious, luckier, luckiest, luckily, buckets, numbers, numbered, numbering, Sun., sirs, shirts, dirtier, dirtiest, birthdays, leaves, leafy, leaks, leaked, leaking, leaky, lead, leads, led, heat, heats, heated, heater, scolds, scolded, scolding, old, older, hold, holds, held, posters

IV. Sort Your Words.

a. Write each of the spelling words in the correct box.

One-syllable Words

1. _____
2. _____
3. _____
4. _____
5. _____

Two-syllable Words

1. _____
2. _____
3. _____
4. _____
5. _____
6. _____
7. _____
8. _____
9. _____
10. _____
11. _____
12. _____
13. _____

b. By adding endings to the spelling words, make four three-syllable **Other Word Forms** (p. 67).

Three-syllable Words

1. _____   3. _____
2. _____   4. _____

V. Break the Code. Use the code to write the spelling words.

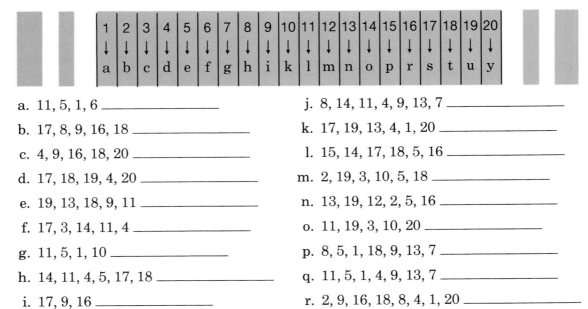

1	2	3	4	5	6	7	8	9	10	11	12	13	14	15	16	17	18	19	20
a	b	c	d	e	f	g	h	i	k	l	m	n	o	p	r	s	t	u	y

a. 11, 5, 1, 6 _____

b. 17, 8, 9, 16, 18 _____

c. 4, 9, 16, 18, 20 _____

d. 17, 18, 19, 4, 20 _____

e. 19, 13, 18, 9, 11 _____

f. 17, 3, 14, 11, 4 _____

g. 11, 5, 1, 10 _____

h. 14, 11, 4, 5, 17, 18 _____

i. 17, 9, 16 _____

j. 8, 14, 11, 4, 9, 13, 7 _____

k. 17, 19, 13, 4, 1, 20 _____

l. 15, 14, 17, 18, 5, 16 _____

m. 2, 19, 3, 10, 5, 18 _____

n. 13, 19, 12, 2, 5, 16 _____

o. 11, 19, 3, 10, 20 _____

p. 8, 5, 1, 18, 9, 13, 7 _____

q. 11, 5, 1, 4, 9, 13, 7 _____

r. 2, 9, 16, 18, 8, 4, 1, 20 _____

Spelling Words

until   study   lucky   bucket   number   Sunday
sir   shirt   dirty   birthday   leaf   leak   leading
heating   scold   oldest   holding   poster

VI. Scrambled Words. Unscramble each scrambled word to find the spelling word that completes the sentence. Write the word.

Scrambled Words

a. This has really been my _____ day.   yckul

b. Who is that with the _____ face?   drtyi

c. A _____ just fell from the oak tree.   flae

d. I carefully put on my _____ and tie.   irtsh

e. I got up early on _____ morning.   dySaun

f. Who is the _____ in our class?   stldoe

g. My _____ is in April.   rthibdya

h. You should _____ the naughty puppy.   ldosc

i. There's a _____ in this pail.   keal

j. The guide is _____ the way through the woods.   ngdeali

k. We have enough fuel for _____ the house.   ngteahi

l. Our class drew a _____ for the school play.   sterop

m. We use the word _____ to begin many letters.   ris

n. Are you _____ on to the rope as tightly as you can?   ngldohi

o. You should _____ for the spelling test.   dyust

p. What is the _____ after 49?   mbuner

q. I will wait _____ tomorrow.   nulit

r. Can you lift this _____ of water?   ckteub

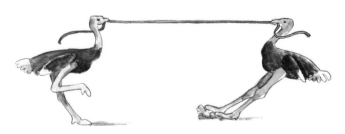

VII. Words and Meanings. Write a spelling word for each meaning. Check your answers in the **Glossary/SPELLEX®**.

a. a day of the week _____

b. a thin, flat part of a plant _____

c. up to the time of _____

d. a round container for carrying things _____

e. to try to learn _____

f. a hole that lets something in or out by accident _____

g. making warm _____

h. having lived for the longest time _____

i. being ahead of _____

j. a piece of clothing for the upper body _____

k. the day on which someone is born _____

l. a large printed notice _____

m. a numeral connected with a person or thing _____

n. taking and keeping in one's hands _____

o. to blame angrily _____

p. having good fortune _____

q. unclean _____

r. a title used instead of a man's name _____

VIII. Final Test. Write each spelling word.

1	2	3	4	5
mist	early	lightning	September	wear
mix	heard	Tuesday	Sunday	November
March	lightly	ahead	until	weak
Wednesday	during	already	holding	farther

I. **Weather Watch.** Write other word forms or the spelling words to complete these sentences about weather. The number tells you in what column you can find the spelling word. Write each word or its other word form only once. If you need help, use the **Glossary/SPELLEX**®.

a. The snowstorm came (2) __ __ __ __ __ __ __ than we expected.

b. Thunder and (3) __ __ __ __ __ __ __ __ __ are coming our way.

c. A (1) __ __ __ __ __ fog rolled off the ocean.

d. There were a few sunny days in the month of (4) __ __ __ __ __ __ __ __ __ .

e. You will be (5) __ __ __ __ __ __ __ coats tomorrow if it gets colder.

f. For the holiday on (4) __ __ __ __ __ __ , there will be clear skies.

g. We will be (2) __ __ __ __ __ __ __ thunder later on today.

h. The month of (5) __ __ __ __ __ __ __ __ was filled with sunny days.

i. Rain (1) __ __ __ __ __ with snow is forecasted.

j. On (3) __ __ __ __ __ __ __ there is a chance of freezing rain.

k. There will be a (2) __ __ __ __ __ snowfall tonight.

l. As the storm got closer, it got (5) __ __ __ __ __ __ in strength.

m. A strong (1) __ __ __ __ __ wind will bend the trees.

n. It will be 24 hours (4) __ __ __ __ __ the rain stops.

o. The clouds up (3) __ __ __ __ __ look very dark.

p. The latest map shows the storm moving (5) __ __ __ __ __ __ __ out to sea.

q. The storm will likely (4) __ __ __ __ off until early evening.

r. By noon today, there (3) __ __ __ __ __ __ __ was flooding in the streets.

s. Children missed school on (1) __ __ __ __ __ __ __ __ __ due to the hurricane.

t. Two feet of snow fell (2) __ __ __ __ __ __ the night.

71

18

1	2	3	4	5
oil	dawn	lawn	leak	draw
earn	hammer	heart	tin	few
point	join	thread	leaf	breath
deliver	lean	meal	silver	broke

II. Squaring Off. Add endings to the spelling words. Write the new words in the squares. For some words you need to add or subtract a letter before adding the ending. If you need help, use the **Glossary/SPELLEX®**.

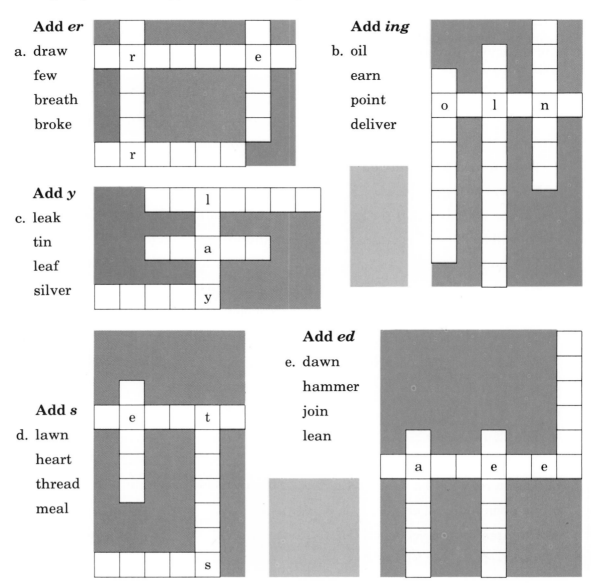

Add er

a. draw

few

breath

broke

Add ing

b. oil

earn

point

deliver

Add y

c. leak

tin

leaf

silver

Add s

d. lawn

heart

thread

meal

Add ed

e. dawn

hammer

join

lean

72

1	2	3	4	5
boil	ladder	marker	score	skating
bucket	laws	mint	shirt	sliding
earth	lucky	music	sir	straw
fears	madder	noise	sixteen	women
froze	marble	river	sixth	writer

III. Hidden Words. Use the clues to find other word forms or the spelling words in the puzzle. Circle and write each word.

```
b o i l i n g c m a r b l e s
u p l a d d e r s s i w r m h
c e o w s k a t e d v z d o i
k m n a r j i m t v e b n s r
e a r t h d b i u w r q p e t
t o f e a r x n o r s i x c s
s i x t e e n t h m a d n a m
f r e e z e o m u s i c i a n
b z y q u t i n o s l i d e s
l u c k i e s t r a w y z w i
s c o r e d e m a r k s t b r
w r i t e x s w o m a n c t u
```

Across

a. bubbling hot

— — — — — — —

b. polished round stones

— — — — — — —

c. used for climbing

— — — — — —

d. moved on ice — — — — — —

e. our planet — — — — —

f. to feel afraid — — — —

g. after five — — —

h. after the fifteenth

— — — — — — —

i. angry — — —

j. to make water into ice

— — — — — —

k. violinist — — — — — — —

l. moves on a smooth surface

— — — — — — —

m. having the best luck

— — — — — — — — —

n. stalks of grain — — — — —

o. made points in a game

— — — — —

p. spots on a paper — — — — —

q. to make words with a pen

— — — — — —

r. an adult female — — — — —

Down

a. used to carry sand

— — — — — — —

b. a rule — — —

c. unpleasant sounds

— — — — — —

d. a plant used for flavoring

— — — —

e. streams of water

— — — — — —

f. clothing that has sleeves

— — — — — —

g. a title for a man — — —

18

1	2	3	4	5
bid	dim	leading	porch	shining
birthday	dirty	matter	poster	sliced
chart	driving	number	replace	soil
coin	globe	oldest	reward	study
death	heating	plane	scold	ticket

IV. Word Arithmetic. Make one or two changes on each spelling word to write another word form.

a. replace – e + ing = _____

b. plane + s = _____

c. shining – ing + es = _____

d. number + ed = _____

e. oldest – est + er = _____

f. bid + d + er = _____

g. sliced – ed + ing = _____

h. death + ly = _____

i. study – y + ies = _____

j. poster + s = _____

k. reward + ed = _____

l. soil + s = _____

m. matter + ed = _____

n. porch + es = _____

o. heating – ing + ed = _____

p. dim + ly = _____

q. coin + ed = _____

r. globe – e + al = _____

s. scold + s = _____

t. birthday + s = _____

u. chart + ed = _____

v. ticket + ing = _____

w. driving – ing + es = _____

x. leading – ing + s = _____

y. dirty – y + ier = _____

WANTED
The Tin Can Caper
Billy Goat
$1 Reward

WANTED
for The Honey Heist
"Grizzly" Bear
$5000 Reward

WANTED
The Great Peanut Robbery
"Dumbo" Elephant
$1,000,001 Reward

Lesson 19

I. Check Test. Write each spelling word.

II. Spelling Words and Phrases

iron	to **iron** the clothes
island	small **island**
tiny	**tiny** gerbil
quiet	**quiet** evening
Friday	**Friday** night
provide	will **provide** the meal
lamb	heard the **lamb**
wrap	to **wrap** the package
crack	through the **crack**
crash	will **crash** to the floor
flash	done in a **flash**
drank	**drank** too fast
blanket	favorite **blanket**
glasses	wears **glasses**
led	**led** them away
fled	**fled** from the room
shed	hidden in the **shed**
monster	my pet **monster**

III. Find a Fit. Write each word in its correct shape.

a.
b.
c.
d.
e.
f.
g.
h.
i.
j.
k.
l.
m.
n.
o.
p.
q.
r.

Other Word Forms
irons, ironed, ironing, islands, tinier, tiniest, quietly, quieter, quietest, Fri., provides, provided, providing, provider, lambs, wraps, wrapped, wrapping, cracks, cracked, cracking, crashes, crashed, crashing, flashes, flashed, flashing, drink, drinks, drinking, drunk, blankets, blanketed, blanketing, glass, glassy, lead, leads, leading, flee, flees, fleeing, sheds, shedding, monsters, monstrous

IV. Word Match-ups. Find a word in the spelling list that best fits each phrase. Check your answers in the **Glossary/SPELLEX®**.

a. used to see better _____

b. ran away _____

c. land with water all around _____

d. used on a bed to keep warm _____

e. an ugly movie character _____

f. unlucky day when it's 13 _____

g. very small _____

h. to cover with paper and tie up _____

i. a little storage building _____

j. opposite of *followed* _____

k. a noisy fall _____

l. without noise _____

m. swallowed milk _____

n. a long, narrow opening _____

o. a baby sheep _____

p. a quick, bright light _____

q. used to press clothes _____

r. to give what is needed _____

76

Lesson 20

I. Check Test. Write each spelling word.

II. Spelling Words and Phrases

beef	all **beef** frankfurt
heel	**heel** of my boot
sheep	frolicking **sheep**
steep	down the **steep** path
agree	if you **agree**
cheer	stood up to **cheer**
jar	**jar** of cream
yard	in the front **yard**
harm	no **harm** done
party	invited to the **party**
partly	**partly** completed
candle	lighted **candle**
handle	broom **handle**
paddle	will **paddle** up the stream
saddle	an old western **saddle**
banner	the school **banner**
battle	a **battle** for first place
cattle	**cattle** on the range

III. Find a Fit. Write each word in its correct shape.

a.
b.
c.
d.
e.
f.
g.
h.
i.
j.
k.
l.
m.
n.
o.
p.
q.
r.

Other Word Forms

beefy, heels, heeled, sheepish, steeper, steepest, agrees, agreed, agreeing, agreeable, cheers, cheered, cheering, cheery, cheerful, jars, jarred, jarring, yards, harms, harmed, harming, harmful, parties, partying, part, parts, parted, parting, candles, handles, handled, handling, paddles, paddled, paddling, saddles, saddled, saddling, banners, battles, battled, battling

79

IV. Words and Meanings. Write a spelling word for each meaning. Check your answers in the **Glossary/SPELLEX®**.

a. an animal with thick wool and hooves _____

b. an area of ground around a house _____

c. meat from cattle _____

d. a fight _____

e. to give a happy shout _____

f. having an almost straight up-and-down slope _____

g. the part of an object held by the hand _____

h. to think the same as another _____

i. a seat for riding on a horse _____

j. part of a shoe _____

k. a flag _____

l. to move a canoe with an oar _____

m. cows and bulls _____

n. a glass or clay container _____

o. in part _____

p. a stick of wax with a wick _____

q. people gathered to have fun _____

r. damage or injury _____

V. Hinky Pinky. The solution to each Hinky Pinky is two rhyming words, each with two syllables. Solve each Hinky Pinky. At least one word of each Hinky Pinky will be a spelling word.

Example: This is a very strong tall building. _____*power tower*_____

a. This holds something that gives light in darkness. _____

b. Two cows' fighting is called this. _____

c. This is an event for bright people. _____

d. A riding cowboy uses this to budge his horse. _____

e. This is a person who plans a pattern for a flag. _____

Spelling Words

beef   heel   sheep   steep   agree   cheer   jar   yard   harm   party   partly   candle   handle   paddle   saddle   banner   battle   cattle

VI. Sort Your Words. In alphabetical order, write the spelling words in the correct boxes.

Words With an *ar*	Words With Two *e*'s	Words With an *le* Ending
1. _____	1. _____	1. _____
2. _____	2. _____	2. _____
3. _____	3. _____	3. _____
4. _____	4. _____	4. _____
5. _____	5. _____	5. _____
	6. _____	6. _____

Write the one word not used above. _____

VII. Break the Code. Use the code to write the spelling words.

a	b	c	d	e	f	g	h	i	j	k	l	m
↕	↕	↕	↕	↕	↕	↕	↕	↕	↕	↕	↕	↕
z	y	x	w	v	u	t	s	r	q	p	o	n

a. xzmwov   _____

b. kzwwov   _____

c. qzi   _____

d. xzggov   _____

e. szin   _____

f. ztivv   _____

g. svvo   _____

h. yzmmvi   _____

i. kzigb   _____

j. xsvvi   _____

k. hzwwov   _____

l. kzigob   _____

m. yzggov   _____

n. hsvvk   _____

o. hgvvk   _____

p. szmwov   _____

q. bziw   _____

r. yvvu   _____

VIII. Crazy Clues. Complete the phrases by using the words from the signs.

    a. soup with carrots and _____

    b. the _____ of the shoe

    c. wouldn't _____ a flea

    d. a _____ cloudy day

    e. lumber _____

    f. will _____ up

    g. will _____ to disagree

    h. cookie _____

IX. Lines of Rhymes. Use the word pairs to write two-line rhymes. You may use **Other Word Forms** (p. 79).

    a. sheep—steep

    b. handle—candle

    c. saddle—paddle

    d. cattle—battle

X. Final Test. Write each spelling word.

I. Check Test. Write each spelling word.

II. Spelling Words and Phrases

ton	a **ton** of coal
job	another **job**
sob	a frightened **sob**
fond	**fond** of swimming
chop	a thick lamb **chop**
copy	will **copy** over again
bother	doesn't **bother** me
wrong	**wrong** time
strong	**strong** harness
belonged	**belonged** together
burn	if it will **burn**
nurse	the night **nurse**
purse	found my **purse**
turtle	the sunning **turtle**
returning	**returning** the books
sure	is **sure** of the answer
grind	to **grind** the grain
remind	if you **remind** me

III. Find a Fit. Write each word in its correct shape.

a.
b.
c.
d.
e.
f.
g.
h.
i.
j.
k.
l.
m.
n.
o.
p.
q.
r.

Other Word Forms

tons, jobs, sobs, sobbed, sobbing, fonder, fondest, fondly, chops, chopped, chopping, copies, copied, copying, bothers, bothered, bothering, wronged, wrongly, strongly, stronger, strongest, belong, belongs, belonging, belongings, burns, burned, burning, burner, nurses, nursed, nursing, purses, turtles, return, returns, returned, surest, surely, grinds, ground, grinding, grinder, reminds, reminded, reminding

83

IV. Bases and Suffixes. The spelling list contains sixteen base words and two words with suffixes. Write each spelling word.

Words With Suffixes	Base Words	Words With Suffixes	Base Words
a. tons	_____	j. sobbing	_____
b. nursing	_____	k. bothering	_____
c. jobs	_____	l. reminding	_____
d. chopping	_____	m. fondest	_____
e. copies	_____	n. grinding	_____
f. surest	_____	o. burner	_____
g. purses	_____	p. wrongly	_____
h. turtles	_____	q. _____ belong	
i. strongest	_____	r. _____ return	

V. Guide Words. These word pairs are guide words from the **Glossary/SPELLEX®**. Write the words from the spelling list that appear on the same page as each pair of guide words.

backward—blade
1. _____

blame—bucket
2. _____

build—change
3. _____

chart—corner
4. _____
5. _____

floor—gang
6. _____

get—hate
7. _____

huge—kept
8. _____

nobody—outfit
9. _____

pocket—purse
10. _____

queen—return
11. _____

returning—saves
12. _____

sob—straw
13. _____

stream—thread
14. _____
15. _____

throw—unlock
16. _____
17. _____

worth—yellow
18. _____

Spelling Words

*ton job sob fond chop copy bother wrong
strong belonged burn nurse purse turtle
returning sure grind remind*

VI. Crossword Puzzle. Solve the puzzle by using words from the spelling list. Check your answers in the **Glossary/SPELLEX®**.

Across
1. to trouble or pester
4. was a member of
5. 2,000 pounds
6. to cut with a sharp tool
7. the opposite of *right*
8. a hospital worker
9. a container for money
11. certain
13. to make into powder
14. work that has to be done
15. loving or liking

Down
1. pain from a fire
2. coming back
3. to make someone remember
5. a slow animal
6. one of many of the same
10. not weak
12. to cry

VII. Writing Sentences. Write each set of words in a sentence. You may use **Other Word Forms** (p. 83).

1. nurse—burn

2. sob—purse

3. sure—remind

4. chop—grind

5. strong—ton

6. fond—belonged

7. job—wrong

8. copy—bother

9. turtle—returning

VIII. Final Test. Write each spelling word.

Lesson 22

I. Check Test. Write each spelling word.

II. Spelling Words and Phrases

real	the **real** thing
seat	on the back **seat**
team	the winning **team**
tear	**tear** in my eye
feeling	**feeling** better
meeting	attended the **meeting**
weekend	next **weekend**
between	**between** two slices of bread
coal	lump of hard **coal**
coach	the football **coach**
chose	**chose** a partner
phone	answered the **phone**
stole	if they **stole** it
smoke	smell of **smoke**
spoke	**spoke** harshly
sport	my favorite **sport**
shore	drifted into **shore**
stories	has read more **stories**

III. Find a Fit. Write each word in its correct shape.

a.
b.
c.
d.
e.
f.
g.
h.
i.
j.
k.
l.
m.
n.
o.
p.
q.
r.

Other Word Forms

really, seats, seated, seating, teams, tears, teared, tearing, tearful, feel, feels, felt, meet, meets, met, weekends, coals, coaches, coached, coaching, choose, chooses, chosen, choosing, phones, phoned, phoning, steal, steals, stealing, stolen, smokes, smoked, smoking, smoky, speak, speaks, spoken, speaking, speaker, sports, shores, story

IV. All in a Row. Write the eighteen spelling words in alphabetical order. Then join the boxed letters and write four hidden words.

1. __ __ __ ☐ __ __ __ __
2. __ ☐ __ __ __ __
3. __ __ ☐ __ __ __
4. __ __ __ ☐ __
5. __ __ __ ☐ __ __ __ __

Hidden Word: _____

10. __ ☐ __ __ __ __
11. __ __ ☐ __ __ __
12. __ __ ☐ __ __ __
13. __ ☐ __ __ __ __
14. ☐ __ __ __ __ __

Hidden Word: _____

6. ☐ __ __ __ __ __ __ __
7. __ __ __ __ ☐ __
8. __ __ ☐ __
9. __ __ __ ☐

Hidden Word: _____

15. ☐ __ __ __ __ __ __ __
16. __ ☐ __ __ __
17. __ ☐ __ __
18. __ __ __ __ __ __ __ ☐

Hidden Word: _____

V. Base Words. The spelling list contains twelve base words and six words that are not base words. Write each spelling word.

Words That Are Not Base Words	Base Words	Words That Are Not Base Words	Base Words
a. teams	_____	j. coaches	_____
b. sports	_____	k. tearing	_____
c. seating	_____	l. _____	feel
d. shores	_____	m. _____	meet
e. really	_____	n. _____	story
f. smoking	_____	o. _____	steal
g. coals	_____	p. _____	choose
h. phoned	_____	q. _____	speak
i. weekends	_____		

Write the one base word not used above. _____

Spelling Words

real   seat   team   tear   feeling   meeting   weekend
between   coal   coach   chose   phone   stole
smoke   spoke   sport   shore   stories

VI. Out of Order. The underlined word in each sentence does not make sense because the letters in it are out of order. Rearrange the letters so the sentence makes sense. Write the word change.

a. The <u>stea</u> must be painted again.　　　　＿＿＿＿＿＿＿＿＿＿

b. Children enjoy <u>rosties</u> and fairy tales.　　＿＿＿＿＿＿＿＿＿＿

c. Baseball is a popular <u>rtosp</u>.　　　　　　＿＿＿＿＿＿＿＿＿＿

d. The <u>eamt</u> had a winning season.　　　　＿＿＿＿＿＿＿＿＿＿

e. A <u>eart</u> ran down my face.　　　　　　　＿＿＿＿＿＿＿＿＿＿

f. Is that jewel fake or <u>aler</u>?　　　　　　　＿＿＿＿＿＿＿＿＿＿

g. Clams are found near the <u>reosh</u>.　　　　＿＿＿＿＿＿＿＿＿＿

h. He <u>keosp</u> about your problem.　　　　　＿＿＿＿＿＿＿＿＿＿

i. Who <u>secho</u> the winner?　　　　　　　　＿＿＿＿＿＿＿＿＿＿

j. I will rake the leaves this <u>ndekewe</u>.　　　＿＿＿＿＿＿＿＿＿＿

k. Who is the team's <u>choac</u>?　　　　　　　＿＿＿＿＿＿＿＿＿＿

l. Why are you <u>englife</u> sad?　　　　　　　＿＿＿＿＿＿＿＿＿＿

m. The thief <u>lesto</u> my car.　　　　　　　　＿＿＿＿＿＿＿＿＿＿

n. The <u>nepho</u> did not ring.　　　　　　　＿＿＿＿＿＿＿＿＿＿

o. She wrote <u>tweeben</u> the lines.　　　　　＿＿＿＿＿＿＿＿＿＿

p. The <u>engtime</u> will come to order.　　　　＿＿＿＿＿＿＿＿＿＿

q. Thick <u>kesmo</u> rose from the chimney.　　＿＿＿＿＿＿＿＿＿＿

r. You can burn <u>laco</u> in this stove.　　　　＿＿＿＿＿＿＿＿＿＿

VII. Write Your Journal. Use each of the spelling words or **Other Word Forms** (p. 87) to write a page in your journal about the time you went to see the big game. Circle the spelling words and the other word forms you used.

Date:

VIII. Final Test. Write each spelling word.

Lesson 23

I. Check Test. Write each spelling word.

II. Spelling Words and Phrases

alone	was never **alone**
awoke	**awoke** early
glow	the **glow** of the fire
golden	**golden** sunset
rolled	**rolled** across the floor
hoping	**hoping** to go
nobody	but **nobody** called
greet	will **greet** them at the door
teeth	brushed my **teeth**
indeed	was **indeed** welcome
event	next **event**
level	made it **level**
clever	**clever** stunt
eleven	**eleven** and one
seventh	the **seventh** child
laugh	had to **laugh**
January	a **January** storm
Saturday	going away **Saturday**

III. Find a Fit. Write each word in its correct shape.

a.
b.
c.
d.
e.
f.
g.
h.
i.
j.
k.
l.
m.
n.
o.
p.
q.
r.

Other Word Forms
awake, awakes, awaking, awoken, glows, glowed, glowing, gold, roll, rolls, rolling, roller, hope, hopes, hoped, hopeful, hopefully, greets, greeted, greeting, tooth, toothy, events, eventful, levels, leveled, leveling, cleverer, cleverest, eleventh, seven, laughs, laughed, laughing, laughable, Jan., Sat.

IV. Find the Missing Treasure.
Unscramble the letters in the footprints and discover all the spelling words. The last word is a mystery word. Write the words.

a. vercle   f. vente   k. veell   p. durtaayS

b. pihong   g. yoodnb   l. nthseev   q. deined

c. theet   h. veeenl   m. egret   r. neldog

d. aaurnyJ   i. wogl   n. naloe   s. patier

e. ghaul   j. doller   o. koaew

a. _____   g. _____   m. _____

b. _____   h. _____   n. _____

c. _____   i. _____   o. _____

d. _____   j. _____   p. _____

e. _____   k. _____   q. _____

f. _____   l. _____   r. _____

s. The mystery word names the person who hid the treasure.

He is a _____ .

V. Word Search.
The spelling words can be found in the word puzzle. The words appear across and down. Circle and write the words.

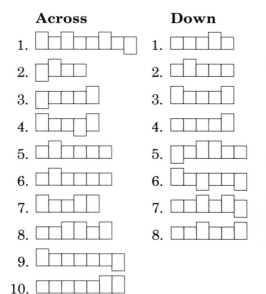

Across

1.
2.
3.
4.
5.
6.
7.
8.
9.
10.

Down

1.
2.
3.
4.
5.
6.
7.
8.

```
a  s  a  t  u  r  d  a  y  t  t  i
w  g  l  o  w  o  g  r  e  e  t  n
o  n  w  v  o  l  a  u  g  h  l  d
k  c  l  e  v  e  r  t  o  o  b  e
e  l  e  v  e  n  x  n  l  p  n  e
a  s  v  e  e  c  d  o  d  i  o  d
l  i  e  n  y  z  c  d  e  n  b  o
o  l  l  t  e  e  t  h  n  g  o  f
n  r  o  l  l  e  d  f  x  u  d  n
e  o  p  r  j  a  n  u  a  r  y  s
t  o  s  e  v  e  n  t  h  o  p  o
```

Spelling Words

*alone awoke glow golden rolled hoping nobody
greet teeth indeed event level clever eleven
seventh laugh January Saturday*

VI. Words and Meanings. Write a spelling word for each meaning. Check your answers in the **Glossary/SPELLEX®**.

a. bright-yellow _____

b. turned over and over _____

c. by oneself _____

d. no person _____

e. to welcome in a friendly way _____

f. light made by a fire _____

g. to make sounds that show happiness _____

h. woke up _____

i. really _____

j. a day of the week _____

k. skillful _____

l. the first month in the year _____

m. wishing _____

n. after the sixth _____

o. one more than ten _____

p. more than one tooth _____

q. at an equal height _____

r. a contest in a sports program _____

93

VII. Writing Sentences. Use each set of words in a sentence about a magic castle. You may use **Other Word Forms** (p. 91).

1. laugh—rolled

2. glow—golden

3. greet—eleven

4. nobody—clever

5. indeed—alone

6. awoke—teeth

7. event—January

8. hoping—seventh

9. level—Saturday

VIII. Final Test. Write each spelling word.

1	2	3	4	5
iron	January	island	blanket	sheep
nurse	banner	party	candle	weekend
team	coach	event	flash	stories
phone	shed	Friday	purse	teeth

I. What's the Name. Write other word forms or the spelling words to name the items below. The number tells you in what column you can find the spelling word. Write each word or its other word form only once. If you need help, use the **Glossary/SPELLEX®**.

a. You use these to keep warm on cold nights. (4) __ __ __ __ __ __ __ __ on a bed

b. This month begins a new year. (2) __ __ __ __ __ __ __

c. These animals grow thick wool. (5) __ __ __ __ __

d. These are heated and used to press clothing. (1) __ __ __ __ __

e. These lands are surrounded by water. (3) __ __ __ __ __ __ __

f. They light up a birthday cake. (4) __ __ __ __ __ __ __

g. You buy these flags at baseball games. (2) __ __ __ __ __ __ __

h. They care for sick people. (1) __ __ __ __ __ __

i. This is the end of every week. (5) __ __ __ __ __ __ __

j. You form these to play football. (1) __ __ __ __ __

k. These are held on birthdays. (3) __ __ __ __ __ __ __

l. You see these bright lights after thunder. (4) __ __ __ __ __ __ __ of lightning

m. They teach people on sports teams. (2) __ __ __ __ __ __ __

n. You read this in a book. (5) __ __ __ __ __

o. These are big happenings. (3) __ __ __ __ __ __

p. You use this to talk to someone. (1) __ __ __ __ __

q. People store garden tools in these. (2) __ __ __ __ __

r. It comes after Thursday. (3) __ __ __ __ __ __

s. People use these to hold items. (4) __ __ __ __ __ __

t. You use these to chew food. (5) __ __ __ __ __

24

1	2	3	4	5
wrap	feeling	crash	glasses	partly
level	meeting	agree	bother	belonged
returning	burn	rolled	greet	glow
hoping	laugh	sport	copy	grind

II. Bases and Endings.

a. Write an other word form for each base word. If you need help, use the **Glossary/SPELLEX®**.

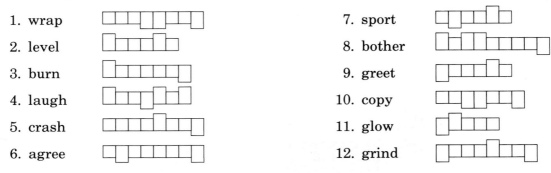

1. wrap

2. level

3. burn

4. laugh

5. crash

6. agree

7. sport

8. bother

9. greet

10. copy

11. glow

12. grind

b. Write the base word and one other word form for each spelling word. If you need help, use the **Glossary/SPELLEX®**.

Spelling Word	Base Word	Other Word Form
Example: returning	r e t u r n	*returned*
1. hoping		_____
2. feeling		_____
3. meeting		_____
4. rolled		_____
5. glasses		_____
6. partly		_____
7. belonged		_____

1	2	3	4	5
awoke	clever	lamb	real	stole
beef	eleven	nobody	saddle	sure
between	handle	paddle	Saturday	turtle
cattle	jar	provide	seat	wrong
cheer	job	quiet	seventh	yard

III. Farmyard Foul-ups. Write other word forms or the spelling words to complete these scenes that you may or may not see at a farm. Write each word or its other word form only once. If you need help, use the **Glossary/SPELLEX**®.

a. ants stuck to __ __ __ __ of honey spilled in the two __ __ __ __ __
   jar   yard

b. __ __ __ __ __ __ ducks __ __ __ __ __ __ __ __ backwards
   seventh   paddle

c. shoes __ __ __ __ __ __ __ for horses but put on the __ __ __ __ __ feet
   provide   wrong

d. children __ __ __ __ __ __ __ chicks __ __ __ __ __ __
   handle   quiet

e. baby __ __ __ __ running __ __ __ __ __ __ mother's legs
   lamb   between

f. cooks __ __ __ __ __ __ __ spicing the __ __ __ __ for the noon meal
   clever   beef

g. __ __ __ __ __ __ dirty pigs that __ __ __ __ __ __ wants to be near
   real   nobody

h. children __ __ __ __ __ __ __ for the __ __ __ __ __ __ __ in the race
   cheer   turtle

i. no __ __ __ __ __ for __ __ __ __ __ __ hens to hatch their eggs
   seat   eleven

j. __ __ __ __ __ __ being __ __ __ __ __ __ __ for horses' __ __ __ __
   cattle   saddle   job

k. a fox __ __ __ __ __ __ planning to return the __ __ __ __ __ __ eggs
   sure   stole

l. roosters __ __ __ __ __ __ early on a __ __ __ __ __ __ __ __
   awoke   Saturday

97

24

1	2	3	4	5
alone	crack	harm	remind	steep
battle	drank	heel	shore	strong
chop	fled	indeed	smoke	tear
chose	fond	led	sob	tiny
coal	golden	monster	spoke	ton

IV. Break the Code. Use the code to write an other word form or a spelling word.

1	2	3	4	5	6	7	8	9	10	11	12	13	14	15	16	17	18
↓	↓	↓	↓	↓	↓	↓	↓	↓	↓	↓	↓	↓	↓	↓	↓	↓	↓
a	b	c	d	e	f	g	h	i	k	l	m	n	o	p	r	s	t

a. ___ ___ ___ ___ ___ ___ ___
  2 1 18 18 11 5 17

b. ___ ___ ___ ___ ___
  11 5 1 4 17

c. ___ ___ ___ ___ ___ ___
  9 13 4 5 5 4

d. ___ ___ ___ ___ ___ ___ ___ ___
  6 14 13 4 13 5 17 17

e. ___ ___ ___ ___
  6 11 5 5

f. ___ ___ ___ ___ ___ ___ ___ ___
  17 18 16 14 13 7 5 16

g. ___ ___ ___ ___ ___
  3 14 1 11 17

h. ___ ___ ___ ___ ___ ___ ___
  18 9 13 9 5 17 18

i. ___ ___ ___ ___ ___ ___ ___
  3 16 1 3 10 5 4

j. ___ ___ ___ ___ ___ ___ ___ ___
  12 14 13 17 18 5 16 17

k. ___ ___ ___ ___ ___ ___ ___
  17 12 14 10 9 13 7

l. ___ ___ ___ ___
  18 14 13 17

m. ___ ___ ___ ___ ___ ___ ___
  16 5 12 9 13 4 17

n. ___ ___ , ___ ___ ___
  18 5 1 16 17

o. ___ ___ ___ ___ ___ ___
  17 15 14 10 5 13

p. ___ ___ ___ ___ ___
  1 11 14 13 5

q. ___ ___ ___ ___ ___ ___ ___
  17 14 2 2 9 13 7

r. ___ ___ ___ ___
  7 14 11 4

s. ___ ___ ___ ___ ___ ___
  17 8 14 16 5 17

t. ___ ___ ___ ___ ___ ___
  8 1 16 12 5 4

u. ___ ___ ___ ___ ___
  4 16 9 13 10

v. ___ ___ ___ ___ ___ ___
  3 8 14 17 5 13

w. ___ ___ ___ ___ ___ ___ ___
  3 8 14 15 15 5 4

x. ___ ___ ___ ___ ___ ___ ___ ___
  17 18 5 5 15 5 17 18

y. ___ ___ ___ ___ ___
  8 5 5 11 17

Lesson 25

I. Check Test. Write each spelling word.

II. Spelling Words and Phrases

peek	to **peek** into the box
queen	dressed like a **queen**
sheet	a flowered **sheet**
steel	**steel** rod
wheel	behind the **wheel**
sweep	to **sweep** into a pile
sleepy	**sleepy** child
flow	**flow** of the river
slowly	crawled **slowly**
throw	the longest **throw**
grown	**grown** older
shown	had **shown** me
owner	found the **owner**
hero	medal for the **hero**
danger	sign of **danger**
ranger	the **ranger** on duty
strange	a **strange** sound
change	too much **change**
chance	not a **chance**
dancing	**dancing** in a circle

III. Find a Fit. Write each word in its correct shape.

a.
b.
c.
d.
e.
f.
g.
h.
i.
j.
k.
l.
m.
n.
o.
p.
q.
r.
s.
t.

Other Word Forms

peeked, peeking, queens, queenly, sheets, steels, steely, wheels, wheeled, swept, sweeping, sleep, sleeps, slept, sleepier, sleepiest, flows, flowed, slow, slowed, slower, slowest, threw, thrown, grow, grows, grew, growing, show, shows, showing, own, owns, owners, heroes, dangerous, range, ranges, ranged, ranging, stranger, strangest, strangely, changed, changing, changeable, chances, dance, dances

IV. Word Ideas. Write the spelling word that best fits each underlined word. Then explain your choice. Use each spelling word only once.

a. <u>Crown</u> makes me think of _____ because...

b. <u>Broom</u> makes me think of _____ because...

c. <u>Adventure</u> makes me think of _____ because...

d. <u>Automobile</u> makes me think of _____ because...

e. <u>River</u> makes me think of _____ because...

f. <u>Singing</u> makes me think of _____ because...

g. <u>Turtle</u> makes me think of _____ because...

h. <u>Medal</u> makes me think of _____ because...

i. <u>Forest</u> makes me think of _____ because...

j. <u>Coins</u> makes me think of _____ because...

k. <u>Being curious</u> makes me think of _____ because...

l. What nine words were left over?

Spelling Words

peek   queen   sheet   steel   wheel   sweep   sleepy
flow   slowly   throw   grown   shown   owner   hero
danger   ranger   strange   change   chance   dancing

V. Bases and Suffixes. The spelling list contains thirteen base words and seven words with suffixes. Write each spelling word.

Words With Suffixes	Base Words		Words With Suffixes	Base Words
a. sweeping	_____	k. wheeled	_____	
b. steely	_____	l. peeking	_____	
c. heroes	_____	m. dangerous	_____	
d. strangely	_____	n. _____	slow	
e. flowed	_____	o. _____	range	
f. changeable	_____	p. _____	grow	
g. queenly	_____	q. _____	show	
h. chances	_____	r. _____	sleep	
i. sheets	_____	s. _____	dance	
j. thrown	_____	t. _____	own	

VI. Three in a Row. Write a spelling word in the group it best fits.

a. prince, king, _____

b. odd, weird, _____

c. tired, drowsy, _____

d. walking, skipping, _____

e. look, stare, _____

f. iron, brass, _____

g. buyer, seller, _____

h. shovel, rake, _____

i. catch, pitch, _____

j. blanket, towel, _____

k. harm, trouble, _____

l. winner, champion, _____

VII. Scrambled Words. Unscramble each scrambled word to find the spelling word that completes the sentence. Write the word.

	Scrambled Words
a. We watched the gentle _____ of the stream.	wofl
b. The bud had _____ into a flower.	wnogr
c. We drove _____ on the icy road.	lslwoy
d. The team had no _____ of winning.	acench
e. The guide had _____ us the way.	ownsh
f. Put a new _____ on this bike.	elewh
g. Will you _____ the tire?	ngeach
h. The forest _____ is in the tower.	ngrear

VIII. Final Test. Write each spelling word.

Lesson 26

I. Check Test. Write each spelling word.

II. Spelling Words and Phrases

shape	triangular **shape**
hate	**hate** to be late
lately	not **lately**
making	**making** lunch
lazy	felt very **lazy**
sharing	**sharing** their toys
careful	**careful** on a bike
careless	**careless** around tools
February	since **February**
tend	**tend** to wait too long
less	much **less**
lesson	next **lesson**
letting	**letting** me sing
friends	some of my **friends**
field	a **field** of daisies
apiece	had three **apiece**
fried	box of **fried** clams
cried	**cried** softly
lying	was caught **lying**
nineteen	**nineteen** minutes

III. Find a Fit. Write each word in its correct shape.

a.

b.

c.

d.

e.

f.

g.

h.

i.

j.

k.

l.

m.

n.

o.

p.

q.

r.

s.

t.

Other Word Forms

shapes, shaping, hates, hated, hateful, late, later, latest, make, makes, made, lazier, laziest, share, shares, shared, care, cares, caring, carelessness, Feb., tends, tended, tending, little, lesser, least, lessen, lessons, let, lets, friend, friendly, friendship, fields, fry, fries, frying, cry, cries, crying, lie, lies, lied, liar, nineteenth

103

IV. All in a Row. Write the twenty spelling words in alphabetical order. Then join the boxed letters and write four hidden words.

1. — ☐ — — — —

2. — — — ☐ — — —

3. — ☐ — — — — — —

4. ☐ — — — —

5. — ☐ — — — — — —

Hidden Word: _____

11. — ☐ — —

12. ☐ — — —

13. ☐ — — — — —

14. — ☐ — — — — —

15. — ☐ — — —

Hidden Word: _____

6. ☐ — — — —

7. — — ☐ — —

8. — — — — ☐

9. ☐ — — —

10. — — — — — ☐

Hidden Word: _____

16. ☐ — — — — —

17. — — — — — ☐ — —

18. — — ☐ — —

19. — — — — ☐ —

20. ☐ — — —

Hidden Word: _____

V. Word Opposites. Antonyms are word opposites. Find the antonym from the spelling list for each word or words below.

a. enemies _____   d. busy _____   g. laughed _____

b. more _____   e. careless _____   h. careful _____

c. love _____   f. truthful _____   i. long ago _____

Spelling Words

shape   hate   lately   making   lazy   sharing   careful
careless   February   tend   less   lesson   letting   friends
field   apiece   fried   cried   lying   nineteen

VI. Base Words. The spelling list contains nine base words and eleven words that are not base words. Write each spelling word.

Words That Are Not Base Words	Base Words		Words That Are Not Base Words	Base Words
a. lessons	_____		k. _____	lie
b. fields	_____		l. _____	friend
c. shaping	_____		m. _____	let
d. nineteenth	_____		n. _____	little
e. tending	_____		o. _____	care
f. Feb.	_____		p. _____	late
g. laziest	_____		q. _____	care
h. hateful	_____		r. _____	make
i. _____	fry		s. _____	share
j. _____	cry			

Write the one base word not used above. _____

VII. Sentence Completion. Complete each sentence with a word from the spelling list.

a. Valentine's Day is always in _____ .

b. I have a piano _____ every week.

c. We planted corn in that _____ .

d. The apples cost a quarter _____ .

e. Twenty is one more than _____ .

f. Chicken tastes best if it's _____ .

g. Who is _____ dinner tonight?

h. My parents are _____ me have a party.

i. I sometimes _____ to work too hard.

j. That box has a funny _____ .

k. We are _____ the last piece of fruit.

VIII. Write Your Journal. Use each of the spelling words or **Other Word Forms** (p. 103) to write a page in your journal about an adventure you once had. Circle the spelling words and the other word forms you used.

IX. Final Test. Write each spelling word.

Lesson 27

I. Check Test. Write each spelling word.

II. Spelling Words and Phrases

cabin	**cabin** in the woods
magic	a **magic** show
habit	a good **habit**
blast	**blast** of the rocket
basket	threw it into the **basket**
absent	never **absent**
fence	painted the **fence**
sense	makes lots of **sense**
cents	forty-five **cents**
center	open in the **center**
December	**December** holiday
plenty	**plenty** of time
twenty	**twenty** miles to go
twenty-five	**twenty-five** days
ripe	almost **ripe**
likely	**likely** to try again
sidewalk	cement **sidewalk**
sideways	**sideways** as a crab
fireplace	in front of the **fireplace**
tired	hot and **tired**

III. Find a Fit. Write each word in its correct shape.

a.
b.
c.
d.
e.
f.
g.
h.
i.
j.
k.
l.
m.
n.
o.
p.
q.
r.
s.
t.

Other Word Forms

cabins, magical, magically, magician, habits, blasts, blasting, baskets, absently, absentee, fences, fenced, fencing, senses, sensed, sensing, senseless, cent, centers, centered, centering, Dec., plentiful, twentieth, twenty-fifth, ripen, ripening, riper, ripest, like, likes, liked, liking, sidewalks, fireplaces, tire, tires, tiring, tiresome, tireless

107

IV. Missing Vowels. Find the missing vowels and write the spelling words.

a. s __ ns __ _____

b. bl __ st _____

c. b __ sk __ t _____

d. h __ b __ t _____

e. f __ nc __ _____

f. t __ r __ d _____

g. r __ p __ _____

h. m __ g __ c _____

i. c __ nts _____

j. pl __ nt __ _____

k. tw __ nt __ _____

l. tw __ nt __ -f __ v __ _____

m. c __ b __ n _____

n. c __ nt __ r _____

o. __ bs __ nt _____

p. l __ k __ l __ _____

q. s __ d __ w __ __ s _____

r. D __ c __ mb __ r _____

s. f __ r __ pl __ c __ _____

t. s __ d __ w __ lk _____

V. Anagrams. Change the letters around in these words to get spelling words.

a. scent _____   b. tried _____   c. pier _____

VI. Compound Words. Join the eight words to form four compound words.

| walk | side | ways | side |
| fire | five | twenty | place |

a. _____   b. _____   c. _____   d. _____

Spelling Words

cabin magic habit blast basket absent fence sense cents center December plenty twenty twenty-five ripe likely sidewalk sideways fireplace tired

VII. Sound-alikes. Write the two homophones from the spelling list.

_____ _____

VIII. Words and Meanings. Write a spelling word for each meaning. Check your answers in the **Glossary/SPELLEX**®.

a. a small, plain house _____

b. the twelfth month of the year _____

c. completely grown and ready for eating _____

d. a wall that protects an area _____

e. good judgment _____

f. done by using tricks _____

g. not present _____

h. a full supply of all that's needed _____

i. an explosion, or loud noise _____

j. a place by the street where people can walk _____

k. an opening that holds a fire _____

l. a woven container _____

m. an action repeated over and over _____

n. half of fifty _____

o. a few pennies _____

p. with one side facing forward _____

q. to be expected _____

r. the middle part of something _____

s. two times ten _____

t. weary, or worn out _____

IX. Complete the Job.

a. Write four spelling words to complete the series.

1. eighteen, nineteen, _____

2. October, November, _____

3. container, holder, _____

4. middle, midpoint, _____

b. Write four spelling words to complete the comparisons.

1. not present, but _____

2. not a few, but _____

3. not a palace, but a _____

4. not unexpected, but _____

c. Write four spelling words to complete the phrases.

1. the _____ of the cannon

2. in the _____ of jogging

3. climbed over the _____

4. a _____ trick

X. All in a Sentence.

Use each of the spelling words in sentences about one of the following titles. You may use **Other Word Forms** (p. 107). Circle the spelling words and the other word forms you used.

A Shopping Trip or A Happy Holiday

Example: *We took a bus to the* (center) *of town.*

XI. Final Test. Write each spelling word.

Lesson 28

I. Check Test. Write each spelling word.

II. Spelling Words and Phrases

busy	should be **busy**
build	would like to **build**
built	**built** of bricks
inch	just one more **inch**
print	large, even **print**
swing	high on the **swing**
living	**living** next door
aid	came to our **aid**
afraid	**afraid** to enter
chain	**chain** on the gate
drain	will **drain** the water
rainy	something for a **rainy** day
mailed	**mailed** the letter
waiting	**waiting** for the bus
repair	will **repair** it soon
oak	an **oak** table
loads	**loads** of lumber
roar	the **roar** of water
board	balanced on the **board**
floor	waxed the **floor**

III. Find a Fit. Write each word in its correct shape.

a.
b.
c.
d.
e.
f.
g.
h.
i.
j.
k.
l.
m.
n.
o.
p.
q.
r.
s.
t.

Other Word Forms
busier, busiest, builds, building, builder, inches, inched, prints, printing, printer, swings, swinging, swung, live, lived, aids, aided, aiding, chains, chained, chaining, drains, draining, rain, rained, raining, rainier, rainiest, mail, mails, mailing, wait, waits, waited, waiter, waitress, repairs, repaired, repairing, oaks, load, loaded, loading, roars, roared, roaring, boards, boarded, boarding, boarder, floors

IV. Sort Your Words. Write each spelling word in the correct box. Two words go in more than one box. Check your answers in the **Glossary/SPELLEX®**.

Words With *ai*	Words With *oa*	Words With a Short *i* Sound
1. _____	1. _____	1. _____
2. _____	2. _____	2. _____
3. _____	3. _____	3. _____
4. _____	4. _____	4. _____
5. _____		5. _____
6. _____		6. _____
7. _____		7. _____
8. _____		8. _____
		9. _____

Write the word that did not fit in any box. _____

V. Base Words. The spelling list contains fourteen base words and six words that are not base words. Write each spelling word.

Words That Are Not Base Words	Base Words	Words That Are Not Base Words	Base Words
a. oaks	_____	k. boarded	_____
b. chains	_____	l. inched	_____
c. building	_____	m. roaring	_____
d. busiest	_____	n. _____	live
e. repaired	_____	o. _____	wait
f. drains	_____	p. _____	mail
g. swinging	_____	q. _____	load
h. aided	_____	r. _____	build
i. floors	_____	s. _____	rain
j. printer	_____		

Write the one base word not used above. _____

Spelling Words

busy build built inch print swing living
aid afraid chain drain rainy mailed waiting
repair oak loads roar board floor

VI. Unscramble and Write. Unscramble each scrambled word to find the spelling word that completes the sentence. Write the word.

Scrambled Words

a. I heard the _____ of the lion.   oarr

b. Did you _____ the broken wheel?   pearri

c. I'm not _____ of the dark.   daifra

d. Every _____ has links.   naich

e. I will _____ the soapy water.   aindr

f. My cousin _____ the letter.   laimed

g. Bees are _____ insects.   suby

h. Did you _____ a snow fort?   lduib

i. We must _____ our names.   ntipr

j. They carried many _____ of books.   doals

k. Today is a _____ day.   niray

l. No _____ is needed to finish the job.   dia

m. The house was _____ in 1860.   ltibu

n. The _____ needs a new seat.   ngisw

o. There are elm and _____ trees in our yard.   koa

p. We are _____ for a friend.   angwiti

q. An _____ is smaller than a foot.   chni

r. One oak _____ is all we need.   bardo

s. A wool rug covers the _____ .   roflo

t. My sister is _____ in Texas.   ingvil

VII. Rewriting as Questions. Rewrite these sentences as questions. The spelling words are underlined.

a. We are <u>living</u> on the fifth <u>floor</u> of that building.

b. We are <u>waiting</u> awhile to <u>build</u> a sand castle.

c. You will <u>repair</u> the <u>drain</u>.

d. They have <u>built</u> the garage with ten <u>loads</u> of lumber.

e. They will put a new <u>chain</u> on the old <u>swing</u>.

f. You were <u>afraid</u> of the lion's <u>roar</u>.

g. An umbrella will <u>aid</u> you on a <u>rainy</u> day.

h. You did <u>print</u> your name on the letter you <u>mailed</u>.

i. The <u>oak</u> tabletop was an <u>inch</u> thick.

j. He is <u>busy</u> putting a <u>board</u> over the window.

VIII. Final Test. Write each spelling word.

Lesson 29

I. Check Test. Write each spelling word.

II. Spelling Words and Phrases

sack	**sack** of potatoes
cash	to **cash** a check
mask	a plain black **mask**
gang	tried to **gang** up
demand	to **demand** a reply
grandmother	**grandmother** and aunt
basketball	a game of **basketball**
none	but there were **none**
front	through the **front** door
above	**above** them all
month	one **month** later
Monday	on a rainy **Monday**
honey	**honey** from the hive
discover	tried to **discover**
recover	will **recover** my breath
thousand	a **thousand** times
amount	very small **amount**
around	**around** the next corner
bound	**bound** with rope
wound	**wound** around their legs

III. Find a Fit. Write each word in its correct shape.

a.
b.
c.
d.
e.
f.
g.
h.
i.
j.
k.
l.
m.
n.
o.
p.
q.
r.
s.
t.

Other Word Forms

sacks, cashes, cashed, cashing, cashier, masks, masked, masking, gangs, demands, demanded, demanding, grandmothers, basketballs, fronts, months, monthly, Mon., honeys, honeyed, discovers, discovered, discovering, discoverer, discovery, recovers, recovered, recovering, recovery, thousands, thousandth, amounts, amounted, amounting, bind, binds, binding, wind, winding

IV. Sort Your Words.

a. Write all the words with a short *a* sound. Check your answers in the **Glossary/SPELLEX®**.

1. _____   4. _____   6. _____

2. _____   5. _____   7. _____

3. _____

Circle the two letters after each short *a* sound.

b. Write all the words with a short *u* sound.

1. _____   4. _____   7. _____

2. _____   5. _____   8. _____

3. _____   6. _____   9. _____

What letter is making this sound? _____

c. Write all the words with the *ou* sound as in *ouch.*

1. _____   3. _____   5. _____

2. _____   4. _____

Circle the word that could also have the *oo* sound as in *boot.*

d. Write the two compound words.

1. _____   2. _____

V. Not This, but That. Use spelling words to complete the phrases below.

a. not a check, but _____

b. not Sunday, but _____

c. not below, but _____

d. not between, but _____

e. not a costume, but a _____

f. not grandfather, but _____

g. not a basket, but a _____

h. not many, but _____

i. not hundred, but _____

j. not back, but _____

k. not ask, but _____

l. not sugar, but _____

m. not one, but a _____

n. not year, but _____

o. not a part, but an _____

p. not hide, but _____

q. not baseball, but _____

r. not lose, but _____

s. not untied, but _____

and _____

Spelling Words

*sack cash mask gang demand grandmother basketball
none front above month Monday honey discover
recover thousand amount around bound wound*

VI. Crossword Puzzle. Solve the puzzle by using words from the spelling list. Check your answers in the **Glossary/SPELLEX®**.

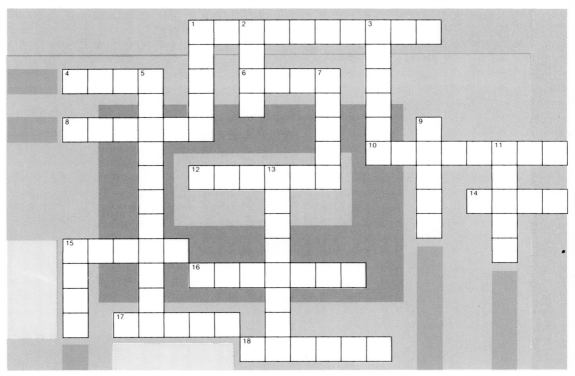

Across
1. a sport played on a court
4. a large group
6. money
8. to ask for strongly
10. ten times one hundred
12. a day of the week
14. not any
15. part of a year
16. to get back something lost
17. the part facing forward
18. in a circle

Down
1. tied
2. a bag
3. the total
5. your father's mother
7. a liquid made by bees
9. wrapped around
11. not below
13. to find out for the first time
15. a face covering

117

VII. Write Your Journal. Use each of the spelling words or **Other Word Forms** (p. 115) to write a page in your journal about a robbery. Circle the spelling words and the other word forms you used.

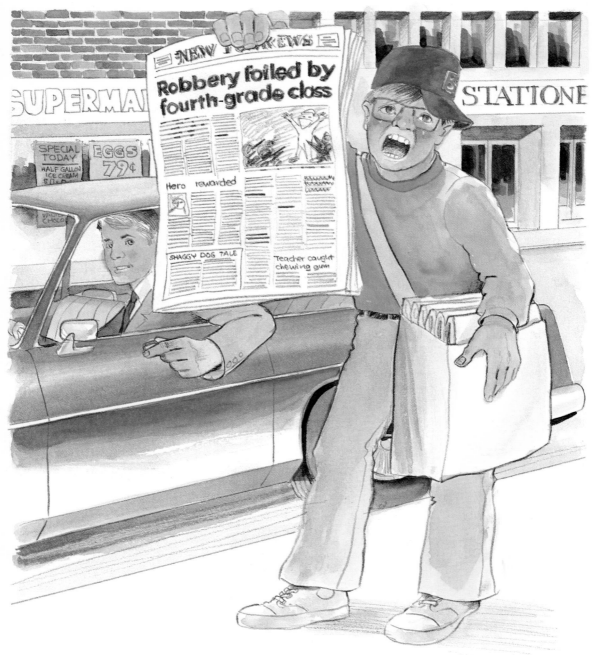

VIII. Final Test. Write each spelling word.

1	2	3	4	5
grown	cried	dancing	bound	lesson
field	cents	friends	basket	fireplace
build	loads	wound	rainy	mailed
honey	waiting	above	gang	grandmother
throw	month	fried	lazy	afraid

I. Words in a Series. Use other word forms or the spelling words to complete each series. The number tells you in what column you can find the spelling word. Use each word or its other word form only once.

a. stayed, rested, (2) __ __ __ __ __ __

b. moves, steps, (3) __ __ __ __ __ __

c. sobbing, weeping, (2) __ __ __ __ __ __

d. days, weeks, (2) __ __ __ __ __ __

e. shower, sprinkle, (4) __ __ __ __

f. becoming, raising, (1) __ __ __ __ __ __ __

g. pastures, meadows, (1) __ __ __ __ __ __

h. bees, sweetener, (1) __ __ __ __ __

i. groups, crowds, (4) __ __ __ __ __

j. buckets, boxes, (4) __ __ __ __ __ __

k. making, stacking, (1) __ __ __ __ __ __ __ __

l. cooking, browning, (3) __ __ __ __ __ __

m. frightened, scared, (5) __ __ __ __ __ __

n. filling, packing, (2) __ __ __ __ __ __

o. assignments, exercises, (5) __ __ __ __ __ __ __

p. pal, person, (3) __ __ __ __ __ __

q. overhead, higher, (3) __ __ __ __ __

r. tossing, pitching, (1) __ __ __ __ __ __ __

s. chimneys, hearths, (5) __ __ __ __ __ __ __ __ __

t. person, relative, (5) __ __ __ __ __ __ __ __ __ __ __

u. tied, knotted, (4) __ __ __ __ __

v. penny, coin, (2) __ __ __ __ __

w. wrap, coil, (3) __ __ __ __

x. tired, slow, (4) __ __ __ __

y. send, postmark, (5) __ __ __ __

30

1	2	3	4	5
absent	December	letting	plenty	sideways
busy	February	likely	ranger	steel
careful	front	Monday	ripe	strange
careless	hero	none	sack	sweep
danger	less	owner	sidewalk	tired

II. Bag of Words. Find the missing letters and write the other word forms. If you need help, use the **Glossary/SPELLEX®**.

The *s* Bag

a. s __ __ __ __ s _____

b. o __ __ __ __ s _____

c. r __ __ __ __ __ s _____

d. d __ __ __ __ __ s _____

e. l __ __ s _____

f. s __ __ __ __ __ s _____

g. t __ __ __ s _____

h. l __ __ __ s _____

i. f __ __ __ __ s _____

j. s __ __ __ s _____

k. s __ __ __ __ s _____

The *er* Bag

a. l __ __ __ er _____

b. r __ __ er _____

c. b __ __ __ __ er _____

The *es* Bag

a. h __ __ __ __ es

_____

The Empty Bag

Write the two words that have no other word forms.

a. s __ __ __ __ __ __ __ _____

b. n __ __ __ _____

The *ful* Bag

a. p __ __ __ __ __ __ ful

_____

The *ly* Bag

a. c __ __ __ __ __ __ __ ly _____

b. s __ __ __ __ __ __ __ ly _____

c. a __ __ __ __ __ __ ly _____

d. c __ __ __ __ __ __ __ ly _____

The Abbreviation Bag

a. F __ __ __ . _____

b. M __ __ __ . _____

c. D __ __ __ . _____

120

1	2	3	4	5
slowly	sharing	drain	twenty	oak
sheet	making	nineteen	built	thousand
queen	lately	cabin	swing	around
sleepy	apiece	magic	floor	basketball
shown	lying	habit	living	twenty-five

III. What a Feeling! Write other word forms or the spelling words to complete these ideas that could make you feel good. The number tells you in what column you can find the spelling word. Write each word or its other word form only once. If you need help, use the **Glossary/SPELLEX®**.

a. playing (5) __ __ __ __ __ __ __ __ __ on a warm spring day

b. pretending to be a (1) __ __ __ __ __ who (4) __ __ __ __ __ in a castle

c. getting into a bed freshly (2) __ __ __ __ with clean (1) __ __ __ __ __ __

d. finding only (5) __ __ __ __ __ __-__ __ __ __ questions instead of one
   (5) __ __ __ __ __ __ __ __ on your math test.

e. (4) __ __ __ __ __ __ __ __ a fence (5) __ __ __ __ __ __ your garden

f. smelling the pine (4) __ __ __ __ __ __ in a summer (3) __ __ __ __ __

g. (1) __ __ __ __ __ __ __ a (3) __ __ __ __ __ trick and having it work

h. waking your (1) __ __ __ __ __ __ __ __ brother so he isn't
   (2) __ __ __ __ for school

i. selling your homemade bookmarks for (4) __ __ __ __ __ __ cents
   (2) __ __ __ __ __ __ at the school fair

j. having (3) __ __ __ __ __ __ __ __ cookies to (2) __ __ __ __ __

k. having your teacher say that your study (3) __ __ __ __ __ __ have
   (1) __ __ __ __ __ __ improved

l. (4) __ __ __ __ __ __ __ __ on a tire under the (5) __ __ __ tree

m. finding out that your friend did not (2) __ __ __ to you

n. fixing the clogged (3) __ __ __ __ __ in the kitchen sink

1	2	3	4	5
change	peek	center	aid	mask
hate	tend	roar	shape	repair
chance	blast	board	demand	recover
wheel	sense	chain	amount	print
flow	fence	inch	cash	discover

IV. Word Building. Add word parts to each spelling word to make other word forms. If you need help, use the **Glossary/SPELLEX®**.

Spelling Words	*s* or *es*	*ed*	*ing*
Example: walk	*walks*	*walked*	*walking*
a. blast			
b. chain			
c. hate			
d. peek			
e. aid			
f. print			
g. change			
h. fence			
i. demand			
j. mask			
k. tend			
l. center			
m. amount			
n. repair			
o. wheel			
p. sense			
q. inch			
r. shape			
s. recover			
t. flow			
u. roar			
v. cash			
w. board			
x. chance			
y. discover			

Lesson 31

I. Check Test. Write each spelling word.

II. Spelling Words and Phrases

pool	jumped into the **pool**
loop	**loop** in the rope
root	**root** of the plant
tooth	chipped a front **tooth**
bloom	will **bloom** in spring
speak	when you **speak**
dream	unusual **dream**
feast	the holiday **feast**
beast	**beast** in the jungle
cable	a new **cable** car
stable	cleaning the **stable**
paste	wallpaper **paste**
waste	threw away the **waste**
attic	in the dusty **attic**
address	new **address**
happening	**happening** to me
sitting	**sitting** very straight
bigger	not much **bigger**
pillow	fluffed up the **pillow**
middle	**middle** of the night

III. Find a Fit. Write each word in its correct shape.

a.
b.
c.
d.
e.
f.
g.
h.
i.
j.
k.
l.
m.
n.
o.
p.
q.
r.
s.
t.

Other Word Forms

pools, loops, looped, looping, roots, rooted, rooting, teeth, toothy, blooms, bloomed, blooming, speaks, spoke, spoken, speaking, dreams, dreamed, dreaming, dreamer, dreamt, feasts, feasted, feasting, beasts, beastly, cables, cabled, stables, stabled, pastes, pasted, pasting, wastes, wasted, wasting, wasteful, attics, addresses, addressed, happen, happens, happened, sit, sits, sat, big, biggest, pillows

123

IV. Sort Your Words. In alphabetical order, write the spelling words in the correct boxes.

Words With Double Consonants

1. _____
2. _____
3. _____
4. _____
5. _____
6. _____
7. _____

Words With Double Vowels

1. _____
2. _____
3. _____
4. _____
5. _____

Words With a Long *a* Sound

1. _____
2. _____
3. _____
4. _____

Words With a Long *e* Sound

1. _____
2. _____
3. _____
4. _____

V. Word Relatives. Write the word from the spelling list that is related to each word or words below.

a. garbage _____

b. animal _____

c. nightmare _____

d. street _____

e. ribbon _____

f. flower _____

g. talk _____

h. taking place _____

i. bed _____

j. carrot _____

k. chew _____

l. top floor _____

m. center _____

n. chair _____

o. glue _____

p. meal _____

q. larger _____

r. barn _____

s. swimming _____

t. rope _____

Spelling Words

pool loop root tooth bloom speak dream feast
beast cable stable paste waste attic address
happening sitting bigger pillow middle

VI. Guide Words. These word pairs are guide words from the **Glossary/SPELLEX®.** Write the words from the spelling list that appear on the same page as each pair of guide words.

above—ax

1. _____

2. _____

backward—blade

3. _____

4. _____

blame—bucket

5. _____

build—change

6. _____

dirty—evening

7. _____

event—flock

8. _____

get—hate

9. _____

leaf—lucky

10. _____

mean—nineteen

11. _____

outfits—plum

12. _____

13. _____

pocket—purse

14. _____

returning—saves

15. _____

shell—sitting

16. _____

sob—straw

17. _____

18. _____

throw—unlock

19. _____

until—worry

20. _____

VII. Hide and Seek. The spelling words can be found in the word puzzle. The words appear across and down. Circle and write the words.

Across

1.
2.
3.
4.
5.
6.
7.
8.

h	a	s	p	e	a	k	m	i	d	d	l	e

```
h  a  s  p  e  a  k  m  i  d  d  l  e
m  n  p  o  o  l  p  j  l  b  m  o  l
s  p  o  k  d  b  j  s  e  i  w  o  b
a  h  a  p  p  e  n  i  n  g  a  p  l
d  t  m  a  i  a  a  t  i  g  s  c  o
d  o  l  s  l  s  t  t  c  e  t  c  o
r  o  o  t  l  t  t  i  d  r  e  a  m
e  t  m  e  o  f  i  n  r  m  t  b  p
s  h  r  f  w  t  c  g  g  u  e  l  k
s  f  e  a  s  t  s  t  a  b  l  e  y
```

Down

1.
2.
3.
4.
5.
6.
7.
8.
9.
10.
11.
12.

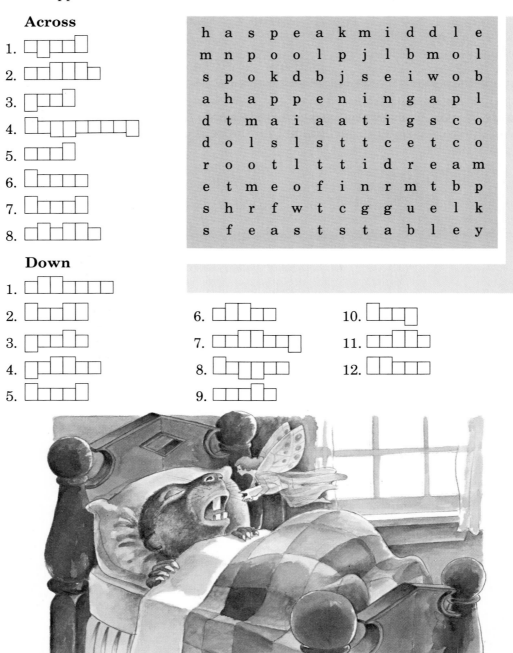

VIII. Final Test. Write each spelling word.

I. Check Test. Write each spelling word.

II. Spelling Words and Phrases

color	a bright **color**
among	**among** their friends
another	to one **another**
anybody	if **anybody** knows
follow	tried to **follow**
gotten	had **gotten** lost
October	cool **October** day
orange	peeled the **orange**
beat	a **beat** of the drum
means	whatever it **means**
reader	the next **reader**
season	in any **season**
leaving	**leaving** shortly
nearest	to the **nearest** phone
ray	a **ray** of sunshine
May	in the month of **May**
playmate	with my **playmate**
always	**always** smiling
sank	**sank** into the sea
fallen	a **fallen** apple

III. Find a Fit. Write each word in its correct shape.

a.
b.
c.
d.
e.
f.
g.
h.
i.
j.
k.
l.
m.
n.
o.
p.
q.
r.
s.
t.

Other Word Forms

colors, coloring, amongst, follows, followed, following, follower, get, gets, got, getting, Oct., oranges, beats, beaten, beating, mean, meant, meaning, read, reads, reading, seasons, seasonal, leave, leaves, left, near, nearer, nearly, rays, playmates, sink, sinks, sunk, sinking, fall, falls, fell, falling

IV. Missing Vowels. Find the missing vowels and write the spelling words.

a. g __ tt __ n _____
b. m __ __ ns _____
c. f __ ll __ w _____
d. c __ l __ r _____
e. r __ __ _____
f. __ m __ ng _____
g. s __ nk _____
h. f __ ll __ n _____
i. b __ __ t _____
j. M __ __ _____

k. __ r __ ng __ _____
l. __ lw __ __ s _____
m. __ ct __ b __ r _____
n. r __ __ d __ r _____
o. n __ __ r __ st _____
p. pl __ __ m __ t __ _____
q. __ n __ th __ r _____
r. __ n __ b __ d __ _____
s. l __ __ v __ ng _____
t. s __ __ s __ n _____

V. Hideaway. Words from the spelling list are hiding in the underlined words in each sentence. Circle the words. Write the words.

a. Can you dis (play mate) rial for the sale? _____
b. Spring and fall entice many tourists to the mountains. _____
c. The captain sailed the seas on a ship. _____
d. Bankers dread errors being made in money matters. _____
e. The tube attached to the beaker is broken. _____
f. The skater's ankle was swollen. _____
g. The boss knows several ways to solve problems. _____
h. The farmer fears no ranges will be left for cattle. _____
i. The extra yam must be eaten. _____
j. He turns on that spigot ten times a day. _____
k. That dog is a mongrel. _____
l. Please give me answers to the questions. _____
m. Walk by the sea not here by the dunes. _____
n. Gone are stories of the wild West. _____

Spelling Words

color among another anybody follow gotten October orange beat means reader season leaving nearest ray May playmate always sank fallen

VI. Base Words. The spelling list contains thirteen base words and seven words that are not base words. Write each spelling word.

Words That Are Not Base Words	Base Words		Words That Are Not Base Words	Base Words
a. coloring	_____	i.	_____	fall
b. rays	_____	j.	_____	sink
c. seasonal	_____	k.	_____	mean
d. follower	_____	l.	_____	near
e. beaten	_____	m.	_____	read
f. Oct.	_____	n.	_____	get
g. playmates	_____	o.	_____	leave
h. oranges	_____			

Write the five base words not used above. _____ _____

_____ _____ _____

129

VII. Using Words.

a. Write the five one-syllable spelling words.

_____   _____   _____

_____   _____

Write the five words in sentences about going out in a boat. Try to use **Other Word Forms** (p. 127).

_____

_____

_____

b. Write the one four-syllable spelling word. _____ .

Write the word in a sentence about a telephone call. _____

_____

c. Write the two three-syllable spelling words. _____

_____ . Write the two words in a sentence about pumpkins.

_____

d. Write the twelve two-syllable spelling words.

_____   _____   _____

_____   _____   _____

_____   _____   _____

_____   _____   _____

Write the twelve words in sentences about going to a new school. Try to use **Other Word Forms** (p. 127).

_____

_____

_____

_____

_____

VIII. Final Test. Write each spelling word.

I. Check Test. Write each spelling word.

II. Spelling Words and Phrases

born	**born** nine years ago
fork	**fork** of the tree
fort	built a snow **fort**
forty	**forty** winks
corner	piled in the **corner**
before	**before** you're through
fourth	the **fourth** grade
fourteen	**fourteen** years old
pouring	**pouring** from the pitcher
silk	made of **silk**
sink	dishes in the **sink**
kick	a long, hard **kick**
rich	a **rich** person
film	watched the **film**
windy	high on a **windy** hill
enjoy	for you to **enjoy**
second	in just one **second**
pretend	when they **pretend**
correct	**correct** time
baseball	**baseball** cards

III. Find a Fit. Write each word in its correct shape.

a. ☐☐☐☐
b. ☐☐☐☐
c. ☐☐☐☐
d. ☐☐☐☐
e. ☐☐☐☐
f. ☐☐☐☐☐☐
g. ☐☐☐☐☐☐
h. ☐☐☐☐☐☐☐
i. ☐☐☐☐
j. ☐☐☐☐☐☐
k. ☐☐☐☐☐☐☐
l. ☐☐☐☐
m. ☐☐☐☐☐☐☐☐☐
n. ☐☐☐☐☐☐☐
o. ☐☐☐☐
p. ☐☐☐☐☐☐☐
q. ☐☐☐☐☐
r. ☐☐☐☐☐☐☐
s. ☐☐☐☐☐
t. ☐☐☐☐

Other Word Forms

forks, forked, forts, fortieth, corners, cornered, cornering, four, fourteenth, pour, pours, poured, silky, silken, sinks, sinking, sank, sunk, sunken, kicks, kicked, kicking, richer, richest, richly, films, filmed, filming, wind, windier, windiest, enjoys, enjoyed, enjoying, seconds, seconded, seconding, pretends, pretending, pretended, pretender, corrects, corrected, correcting, baseballs

131

IV. Sort Your Words. In alphabetical order, write the spelling words in the correct boxes. One word goes in two boxes.

Words With *or* or *our*

1. _____ 5. _____ 9. _____
2. _____ 6. _____ 10. _____
3. _____ 7. _____
4. _____ 8. _____

Words in Which *i* Is Followed by Two Consonants

1. _____ 4. _____ 6. _____
2. _____ 5. _____ 7. _____
3. _____

Write the one compound word. _____

Write the spelling words you have not used. _____

_____   _____

V. Three in a Row. Write a spelling word in the group it best fits.

a. edge, end, _____

b. velvet, satin, _____

c. _____ , during, after

d. knife, spoon, _____

e. serving, flowing, _____

f. stormy, rainy, _____

g. stove, refrigerator, _____

h. make-believe, fake, _____

i. football, basketball, _____

j. cartoon, movie, _____

k. life, baby, _____

l. _____ , fifty, sixty

m. love, like, _____

n. second, third, _____

o. money, wealthy, _____

p. _____ , fifteen, sixteen

q. building, castle, _____

r. run, pass, _____

s. first, _____ , third

t. OK, right, _____

Spelling Words

*born   fork   fort   forty   corner   before   fourth
fourteen   pouring   silk   sink   kick   rich   film
windy   enjoy   second   pretend   correct   baseball*

VI. Guide Words. These word pairs are guide words from the **Glossary/SPELLEX®**. Write the words from the spelling list that appear on the same page as each pair of guide words.

backward—blade

1. _____
2. _____

blame—bucket

3. _____

chart—corner

4. _____

correct—dirt

5. _____

dirty—evening

6. _____

event—flock

7. _____

floor—gang

8. _____
9. _____
10. _____
11. _____
12. _____

kick—leading

13. _____

pocket—purse

14. _____
15. _____

returning—saves

16. _____

scale—sheet

17. _____

shell—sitting

18. _____
19. _____

until—worry

20. _____

133

VII. Equal Sides. Use words from the spelling list to make the phrases equal.

a. two weeks = _____ days

b. fancy clothes = _____ shirts

c. April = _____ month

d. eating tools = _____ and knife

e. part of a minute = one _____

f. right reply = _____ answer

g. part of a playing field = _____ diamond

h. scary movie = monster _____

VIII. Hide and Seek. The spelling words can be found in the word puzzle. The words appear across and down. Circle and write the words.

Across

1.
2.
3.
4.
5.
6.
7.
8.
9.

Down

1.
2.
3.
4.
5.
6.
7.
8.
9.
10.
11.

```
                    g  e
                 m  c  n  d
              o  p  r  j  i  i
           v  s  e  c  o  n  d  v
           g  t  i  c  h  y  a  t  a  e
        f  a  b  l  n  b  a  s  e  b  a  l  l  p
        o  l  e  c  k  m  a  r  t  k  o  s  l  r
        u  l  f  o  u  r  t  h  t  b  o  i  b  e
        r  f  o  r  k  r  b  d  a  f  i  l  m  t
        t  o  r  r  i  a  o  t  l  o  a  k  n  e
        e  r  e  e  c  o  r  n  e  r  i  c  h  n
        e  t  h  c  k  q  n  v  e  t  l  o  n  d
        n  r  i  t  c  w  i  n  d  y  w  a  a  c
        c  z  g  d  p  o  u  r  i  n  g  g  n  i
```

IX. Final Test. Write each spelling word.

134

Lesson 34

I. Check Test. Write each spelling word.

II. Spelling Words and Phrases

huge	a **huge** snowdrift
June	was finished last **June**
July	Fourth of **July**
rules	set of **rules**
woman	next to the **woman**
ounce	sold by the **ounce**
pound	89¢ a **pound**
count	to **count** them again
mouse	signs of a **mouse**
hour	an **hour** ago
flour	ground into **flour**
steam	**steam** from the kettle
stream	rushing **stream**
scream	frightened **scream**
sneakers	brand-new **sneakers**
inches	measured in **inches**
since	**since** 1874
picnic	**picnic** basket
picture	hung the **picture**
single	in a **single** file

III. Find a Fit. Write each word in its correct shape.

a.
b.
c.
d.
e.
f.
g.
h.
i.
j.
k.
l.
m.
n.
o.
p.
q.
r.
s.
t.

Other Word Forms

hugest, hugeness, rule, ruled, ruling, ruler, women, womanly, ounces, oz., pounds, lb., counts, counted, counting, counter, mice, hours, hourly, hr., flours, steams, steamer, streams, screams, screamed, screaming, sneaker, inch, inched, inching, in., picnics, picnicking, pictures, pictured, picturing, singly

135

IV. Sort Your Words.

a. Find the missing letters to make spelling words. Write the words.

1. mou __ __   _____
2. __ __ ou __   _____
3. pou __ __   _____
4. ou __ __ __   _____
5. __ ou __   _____
6. cou __ __   _____

How are all these words alike?

b. Find the missing letters to make spelling words.
Write the words.

1. __ t __ ea __   _____
2. __ __ rea __   _____
3. __ __ ea __ __ __ __ _____
4. __ __ ea __   _____

c. Write the spelling words that have a short *i* sound.

1. _____   4. _____
2. _____   5. _____
3. _____

d. Write the spelling words you did not write above.

1. _____   4. _____
2. _____   5. _____
3. _____

V. For Short. Write the spelling word or Other Word Form (p. 135) for each abbreviation.

a. hr. _____   c. lb. _____
b. oz. _____   d. in. _____

Spelling Words

huge   June   July   rules   woman   ounce   pound
count   mouse   hour   flour   steam   stream   scream
sneakers   inches   since   picnic   picture   single

VI. Word Hunt. The spelling words and some **Other Word Forms** (p. 135) can be found in the word puzzle. The words appear across and down. Circle and write the words.

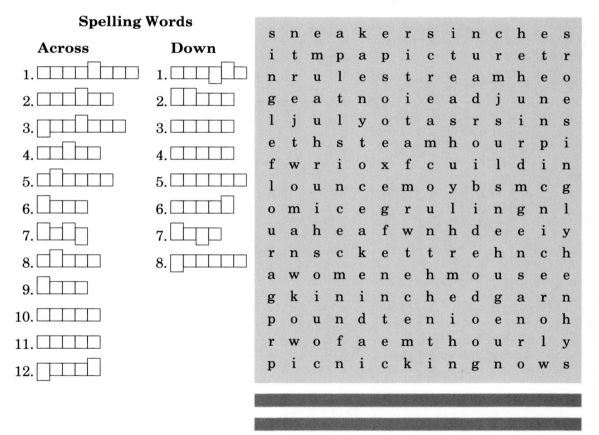

Spelling Words

Across

1.
2.
3.
4.
5.
6.
7.
8.
9.
10.
11.
12.

Down

1.
2.
3.
4.
5.
6.
7.
8.

```
s n e a k e r s i n c h e s
i t m p a p i c t u r e t r
n r u l e s t r e a m h e o
g e a t n o i e a d j u n e
l j u l y o t a s r s i n s
e t h s t e a m h o u r p i
f w r i o x f c u i l d i n
l o u n c e m o y b s m c g
o m i c e g r u l i n g n l
u a h e a f w n h d e e i y
r n s c k e t t r e h n c h
a w o m e n e h m o u s e e
g k i n i n c h e d g a r n
p o u n d t e n i o e n o h
r w o f a e m t h o u r l y
p i c n i c k i n g n o w s
```

Other Word Forms

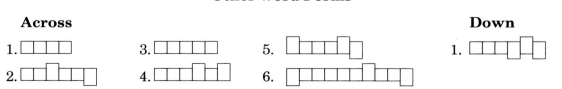

Across

1.
2.
3.
4.
5.
6.

Down

1.

137

VII. Solve the Puzzle. Solve the puzzle by using words from the spelling list. Check your answers in the **Glossary/SPELLEX®**.

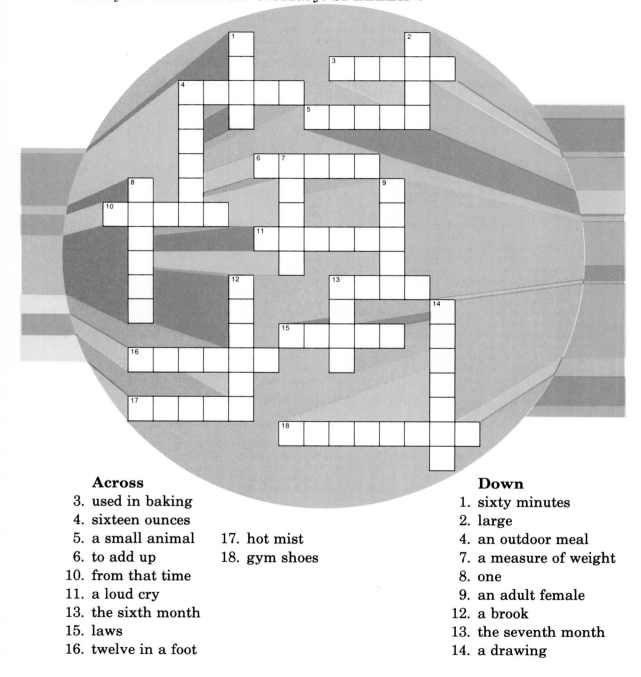

Across

3. used in baking
4. sixteen ounces
5. a small animal
6. to add up
10. from that time
11. a loud cry
13. the sixth month
15. laws
16. twelve in a foot
17. hot mist
18. gym shoes

Down

1. sixty minutes
2. large
4. an outdoor meal
7. a measure of weight
8. one
9. an adult female
12. a brook
13. the seventh month
14. a drawing

VIII. Final Test. Write each spelling word.

I. Check Test. Write each spelling word.

II. Spelling Words and Phrases

omit	if you **omit** two words
only	the **only** one left
ocean	swam in the **ocean**
opening	through the **opening**
poem	a twelve-line **poem**
hotel	staying at the **hotel**
clothes	changed my **clothes**
clothing	**clothing** store
dash	fifty-yard **dash**
ranch	a large **ranch** house
branch	local **branch** of the library
handy	the **handy** tool kit
packed	**packed** too tightly
package	**package** of gum
landing	stepped onto the **landing**
evening	a summer **evening**
fever	a high **fever**
everyone	enough for **everyone**
everybody	if **everybody** knew
everything	mixed **everything** together

III. Find a Fit. Write each word in its correct shape.

a.
b.
c.
d.
e.
f.
g.
h.
i.
j.
k.
l.
m.
n.
o.
p.
q.
r.
s.
t.

Other Word Forms
omits, omitted, omitting, oceans, open, opens, opened, opener, poems, poet, poetry, hotels, cloth, clothe, clothed, dashes, dashed, dashing, rancher, ranches, branches, branched, branching, handier, handiest, handily, pack, packs, packing, packages, packaged, land, lands, landings, evenings, feverish

IV. Break the Code. Use the code to write the spelling words.

a	b	c	d	e	f	g	h	i	j	k	l	m
↕	↕	↕	↕	↕	↕	↕	↕	↕	↕	↕	↕	↕
z	y	x	w	v	u	t	s	r	q	p	o	n

a. lxvzm   __ocean__

b. wzhs   __dash__

c. kzxpztv   __package__

d. slgvo   __hotel__

e. xolgsrmt   __clothing__

f. lmob   __only__

g. lkvmrmt   __opening__

h. uvevi   __fever__

i. vevmrmt   __evening__

j. ozmwrmt   __landing__

k. veviblmv   __everyone__

l. klvn   __poem__

m. xolgsvh   __clothes__

n. lnrg   __omit__

o. vevibgsrmt   __everything__

p. kzxpvw   __packed__

q. szmwb   __handy__

r. yizmxs   __branch__

s. vevibylwb   __everybody__

t. izmxs   __ranch__

V. Word Search. The spelling words can be found in the word puzzle. The words appear across and down. Circle and write the words.

Across

1.
2.
3.
4.
5.
6.
7.
8.
9.
10.
11.

Down

1.
2.
3.
4.
5.
6.
7.
8.
9.

p	c	l	o	t	h	e	s	o	v	e
a	h	o	t	e	l	v	n	n	e	v
c	c	e	s	p	o	e	m	l	r	e
k	s	f	e	v	e	r	o	y	u	r
a	a	e	v	e	r	y	b	o	d	y
g	y	t	e	h	o	t	r	p	a	o
e	h	a	n	d	y	h	g	e	s	n
h	o	m	i	t	n	i	t	n	h	e
v	l	a	n	d	i	n	g	i	r	o
e	s	t	g	m	e	g	p	n	a	c
b	r	a	n	c	h	w	z	g	n	e
f	p	a	c	k	e	d	r	b	c	a
c	l	o	t	h	i	n	g	p	h	n

Spelling Words

omit only ocean opening poem hotel clothes clothing
dash ranch branch handy packed package
landing evening fever everyone everybody everything

VI. Sort Your Words.

a. Sometimes *ing* is an ending added to a base word. Other times *ing* is part of the base word. Write all the spelling words that end in *ing*.

1. _____   3. _____   5. _____

2. _____   4. _____

Of the words you have just written, circle those in which *ing* is an ending added to a base word. If you need help, use the **Glossary/SPELLEX®**.

b. Three spelling words end with the long *e* sound. Write them.

1. _____   2. _____   3. _____

What letter makes the long *e* sound? _____

c. Eight spelling words have a long *o* sound. Write them in alphabetical order.

1. _____   4. _____   7. _____

2. _____   5. _____   8. _____

3. _____   6. _____

d. Seven spelling words have a short *a* sound. Write them in alphabetical order.

1. _____   4. _____   6. _____

2. _____   5. _____   7. _____

3. _____

e. Two spelling words have not been used above. Write them.

1. _____   2. _____

VII. Writing Sentences. Write each set of words in a sentence. You may use **Other Word Forms** (p. 139).

1. landing—ocean

2. fever—evening

3. everybody—dash

4. everyone—hotel

5. omit—package

6. only—poem

7. clothes—ranch

8. clothing—packed

9. branch—handy

10. opening—everything

VIII. Final Test. Write each spelling word.

1	2	3	4	5
pool	playmate	sneakers	cable	ray
root	orange	picture	clothing	address
branch	sink	package	ocean	ranch
attic	baseball	fork	beat	tooth
pillow	stable	hotel	color	film

I. What Do You Need? Write other word forms or the spelling words to complete the items. The numbers tell you in what column you can find the spelling word. Write each word or its other word form only once. If you need help, use the **Glossary/SPELLEX®**.

a. water in a swimming (1) ___ ___ ___ ___

b. friends or (2) ___ ___ ___ ___ ___ ___ ___ ___ ___ to play tag

c. (4) ___ ___ ___ ___ ___ ___ for trolley cars

d. the sun's (5) ___ ___ ___ ___ to warm the earth

e. a (3) ___ ___ ___ ___ ___ ___ ___ with a shoelace that's not broken

f. fresh (2) ___ ___ ___ ___ ___ ___ ___ to make juice

g. (4) ___ ___ ___ ___ ___ ___ ___ to wear to school

h. carrots with healthy (1) ___ ___ ___ ___ ___

i. walls with (3) ___ ___ ___ ___ ___ ___ ___ ___ hanging

j. numbers and streets for (5) ___ ___ ___ ___ ___ ___ ___ ___ ___ on letters

k. pretty paper and bows to wrap (3) ___ ___ ___ ___ ___ ___ ___

l. ovens, refrigerators, and (2) ___ ___ ___ ___ ___ in kitchens

m. large farms or (5) ___ ___ ___ ___ ___ ___ ___ to raise animals

n. (1) ___ ___ ___ ___ ___ ___ ___ ___ on trees to climb

o. large (4) ___ ___ ___ ___ ___ ___ for ships to sail

p. eggs that are (4) ___ ___ ___ ___ ___ ___ to make breakfast

q. (5) ___ ___ ___ ___ ___ for chewing

r. bats and (2) ___ ___ ___ ___ ___ ___ ___ ___ ___ to play a game

s. knives, (3) ___ ___ ___ ___ ___ , and spoons to eat a meal

t. (1) ___ ___ ___ ___ ___ ___ for storing old furniture

u. rooms in (3) ___ ___ ___ ___ ___ ___ for travelers

v. (1) ___ ___ ___ ___ ___ ___ ___ on a bed to lay your head

w. cameras for (5) ___ ___ ___ ___ ___ ___ ___ a movie

x. (4) ___ ___ ___ ___ ___ ___ ___ flags for the parade

y. clean (2) ___ ___ ___ ___ ___ ___ ___ for horses

36

1	2	3	4	5
always	bigger	everything	July	middle
among	born	forty	June	October
another	enjoy	fourteen	leaving	only
anybody	everybody	fourth	May	since
before	everyone	gotten	means	sitting

II. Break the Code. Use the code to write an other word form or a spelling word. Write each word. Remember to use a capital letter for the calendar words.

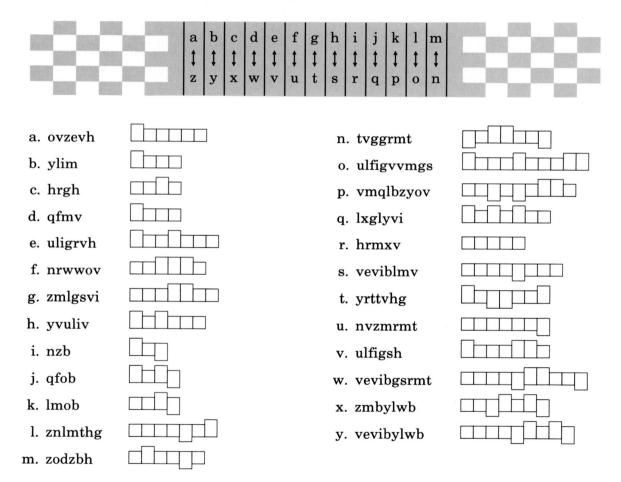

a. ovzevh

b. ylim

c. hrgh

d. qfmv

e. uligrvh

f. nrwwov

g. zmlgsvi

h. yvuliv

i. nzb

j. qfob

k. lmob

l. znlmthg

m. zodzbh

n. tvggrmt

o. ulfigvvmgs

p. vmqlbzyov

q. lxglyvi

r. hrmxv

s. veviblmv

t. yrttvhg

u. nvzmrmt

v. ulfigsh

w. vevibgsrmt

x. zmbylwb

y. vevibylwb

1	2	3	4	5
bloom	dream	huge	paste	sank
clothes	fever	kick	poem	speak
correct	flour	mouse	pound	steam
count	fort	omit	pretend	stream
dash	hour	packed	rich	woman

III. **Word Clues.** Write the spelling word that goes with each clue. The number tells you in what column you can find the spelling word. Then write an other word form for each spelling word. If you need help, use the **Glossary/SPELLEX®**.

Word Clues	Spelling Words	Other Word Forms
a. a rhyming verse (4)	— — — —	_____
b. a sticky mixture (4)	— — — — —	_____
c. to talk (5)	— — — — —	_____
d. a picture seen while sleeping (2)	— — — — —	_____
e. went to the bottom (5)	— — — —	_____
f. to make believe (4)	— — — — — — —	_____
g. right (1)	— — — — — — —	_____
h. a blow with the foot (3)	— — — —	_____
i. a building (2)	— — — —	_____
j. having a lot of money (4)	— — — —	_____
k. flowing water (5)	— — — — — —	_____
l. 60 minutes (2)	— — — —	_____
m. very large (3)	— — — —	_____
n. an adult female (5)	— — — — —	_____
o. a small furry animal (3)	— — — — —	_____
p. to find the total (1)	— — — — —	_____
q. seen from a boiling kettle (5)	— — — — —	_____
r. to leave out (3)	— — — —	_____
s. a high temperature (2)	— — — — —	_____
t. a fast run (1)	— — — —	_____
u. filled with items (3)	— — — — — —	_____
v. worn on the body (1)	— — — — — — —	_____
w. 16 ounces (4)	— — — — —	_____
x. fine powder from grain (2)	— — — — —	_____
y. to flower (1)	— — — — —	_____

	1	**2**	**3**	**4**	**5**
	beast	follow	loop	pouring	second
	corner	handy	nearest	reader	silk
	evening	happening	opening	rules	single
	fallen	inches	ounce	scream	waste
	feast	landing	picnic	season	windy

IV. Pack Your Suitcase. Add, subtract, or do both to write other word forms.

+ ed

a. pouring - ing + ed = _____

b. happening - ing + ed = _____

c. landing - ing + ed = _____

d. rules - es + ed = _____

e. inches - es + ed = _____

f. opening - ing + ed = _____

+ ing

a. reader - er + ing = _____

b. fallen - en + ing = _____

c. nearest - est + ing = _____

+ est

a. silk + i + est = _____

b. windy - y + i + est = _____

c. handy - y + i + est = _____

+ s

a. feast + s = _____

b. loop + s = _____

c. beast + s = _____

d. waste + s = _____

e. follow + s = _____

f. season + s = _____

g. second + s = _____

h. corner + s = _____

i. ounce + s = _____

j. scream + s = _____

k. single + s = _____

l. picnic + s = _____

m. evening + s = _____

SPELLEX® Glossary
Level D

This section of your spelling book is called **SPELLEX® Glossary—Level D**. It is a collection of the spelling words from **Working Words in Spelling—Level D**, together with the phonetic spelling, part of speech, definition, sample phrase, and other word forms for each spelling word.

You will find the **SPELLEX® Glossary** a useful tool in your spelling work and in your everyday writing. It is a valuable resource as you do your spelling exercises and as you practice and review your spelling words. From the groups of other word forms, you can choose the best words to express your ideas or to add variety and smoothness to your writing. The **SPELLEX® Glossary** will give you a quick way to check the spellings and meanings of words.

The **SPELLEX® Glossary** is arranged very simply. All the entry words are listed in alphabetical order. All the spelling words are printed in dark type. If the spelling word is not a base word, you are told what the base word is. With the base word and its definition, you will find the other word forms.

Example: dirt|dûrt| *n.* Dust, mud, or any material that makes something unclean: *dirt on his face.* **dirty, dirtier, dirtiest, dirties, dirtied, dirtying**

dirty |dûr′tē| *adj.* Unclean: *dirty hands.* [see *dirt*]

PRONUNCIATION KEY

ă	pat	j	judge	sh	dish, ship	
ā	aid, fey, pay	k	cat, kick, pique	t	tight	
â	air, care, wear	l	lid, needle	th	path, thin	
ä	father	m	am, man, mum	*th*	bathe, this	
b	bib	n	no, sudden	ŭ	cut, rough	
ch	church	ng	thing	û	circle, firm, heard,	
d	deed	ŏ	horrible, pot		term, turn, urge, word	
ĕ	pet, pleasure	ō	go, hoarse, row, toe	v	cave, valve, vine	
ē	be, bee, easy, leisure	ô	alter, caught, for, paw	w	with	
f	fast, fife, off, phase, rough	oi	boy, noise, oil	y	yes	
g	gag	ou	cow, out	yōō	abuse, use	
h	hat	ōŏ	took	z	rose, size, xylophone, zebra	
hw	which	ōō	boot, fruit	zh	garage, pleasure, vision	
ĭ	pit	p	pop	ə	about, silent, pencil,	
ī	by, guy, pie	r	roar		lemon, circus	
î	dear, deer, fierce, mere	s	miss, sauce, see	ər	butter	

STRESS
Primary stress ′ **bi·ol′o·gy** |bī ŏl′ə jē| Secondary stress ′ **bi′o·log′i·cal** |bī′ə lŏj′ĭ kəl|

A

above |ə **bŭv'**| *prep.* Over or higher than: *above the trees.*

absent |**ăb'**sənt| *adj.* Not present: *absent students.* **absence, absently, absentee**

across |ə **krôs'**| *adv.* From one side to another: *across and over. prep.* To the other side of: *across the river.*

address |ə **drĕs'**| *n.* The place where a person lives or the place to which mail is sent: *his street address.* **addresses, addressed, addressing**

afraid |ə **frād'**| *adj.* Feeling frightened or scared: *afraid to be alone.*

again |ə **gĕn'**| *adv.* One more time: *played the game again.*

agree |ə **grē'**| *v.* To think or feel the same way as another person: *will agree that bananas are yellow.* **agrees, agreed, agreeing, agreeable, agreement**

ahead |ə **hĕd'**| *adv.* In front; farther forward: *will go ahead.*

aid |ād| *n.* Help or assistance: *thankful for their aid. v.* To help or give support to: *will aid the teacher.* **aids, aided, aiding**

alike |ə **līk'**| *adv.* In the same way: *to walk alike. adj.* The same; similar: *to be alike in many ways.* **alikeness**

almost |**ôl'**mōst| *adv.* Close to or nearly: *almost time to begin.* **most, mostly**

alone |ə **lōn'**| *adj.* Without company; by oneself: *was alone in the dark.*

already |ôl **rĕd'**ē| *adv.* By a certain time: *already finished.*

always |**ôl'**wāz| *adv.* At all times: *always sunny.*

among |ə **mŭng'**| *prep.* In the company of others: *among the animals in the zoo.* **amongst**

amount |ə **mount'**| *n.* The total or sum: *amount of snow.* **amounts, amounted, amounting**

another |ə **nŭ**th**'**ər| *pron.* One more or a different one: *asked for another.*

anybody |**ĕn'**ē bŏd'ē| *pron.* Any person: *if anybody can go.*

apiece |ə **pēs'**| *adv.* Each; for each one: *ten cents apiece.*

arithmetic |ə **rĭth'**mə tĭk| *n.* Adding, subtracting, multiplying, and dividing: *mistake in my arithmetic.* **arithmetical**

around |ə **round'**| *prep.* **1.** On the farther side of: *around the second bend.* **2.** In a circle about: *around the tree.*

attic |**ăt'**ĭk| *n.* The space just underneath the roof of a house: *stored in the attic.* **attics**

awake |ə **wāk'**| *v.* To wake up: *will awake early.* **awakes, awaked, awoke, awaking**

awoke |ə **wōk'**| *v.* Woke up: *awoke from a dream.* [see *awake*]

ax |ăks| *n.* A tool with a sharp blade, used for chopping wood: *the firefighter's ax.* **axes, axed, axing**

ă pat / ā pay / â care / ä father / ĕ pet / ē be / ĭ pit / ī pie / î fierce / ŏ pot / ō go / ô paw, for / oi oil / ŏŏ book / ōō boot / ou out / ŭ cut / û fur / *th* the / th thin / hw which / zh vision / ə ago, item, pencil, atom, circus
©1977 by Houghton Mifflin Company. Reprinted by permission from THE AMERICAN HERITAGE SCHOOL DICTIONARY.

B

backward |băk′wərd| *adj.* Moving toward the rear: *backward fall.* ***backwards***

banner |băn′ər| *n.* A flag: *a striped banner.* ***banners***

baseball |bās′bôl′| *adj.* Of or for baseball: *baseball mitt.* *n.* A game played with a ball and bat by two teams with nine players on a field with four bases: *new bat for baseball.* ***baseballs***

basket |băs′kĭt| *n.* A woven container: *a laundry basket.* ***baskets***

basketball |băs′kĭt bôl′| *n.* A game played on a court by two teams of five players who try to toss a ball through a basket open at the bottom: *plays basketball and tennis.* ***basketballs***

battle |băt′l| *n.* A fight: *an exciting battle.* ***battles, battled, battling, battler***

be |bē| *v.* To act in a certain way: *to be late.* ***am, is, are, was, were, being, been***

beast |bēst| *n.* A four-footed animal: *a wild beast.* ***beasts, beastly***

beat |bēt| *n.* A stroke, blow, or sound made again and again: *beat of the band.* ***beats, beaten, beating, beater***

beef |bēf| *adj.* Made of beef: *beef stew.* *n.* Meat from a cow, bull, or steer: *roast beef.* ***beefy***

before |bĭ fôr′| *conj.* Ahead of the time when: *before you arrive.*

began |bĭ găn′| *v.* Started: *began to run.* [see *begin*]

begin |bĭ gĭn′| *v.* To start: *will begin to rain.* ***begins, began, begun, beginning, beginner***

begun |bĭ gŭn′| *v.* Started: *since dinner has begun.* [see *begin*]

being |bē′ĭng| *v.* Acting in a certain way: *being very rude.* [see *be*]

belong |bĭ lông′| *v.* **1.** To have a proper place: *to belong here.* **2.** To be a member of: *does belong to the club.* ***belongs, belonged, belonging, belongings***

belonged |bĭ lôngd′| *v.* **1.** Had a proper place: *belonged in the cupboard.* **2.** Was a member of: *belonged to our group.* [see *belong*]

bend |bĕnd| *v.* To curve or make crooked: *will bend the metal.* *n.* A part that is not straight: *a bend in the wire.* ***bends, bent, bending, bendable***

between |bĭ twĕn′| *prep.* In the space dividing two objects or places: *between the trees.*

bid |bĭd| *v.* To offer to pay or buy at a certain price: *will bid ten dollars.* ***bids, bidding, bidder***

big |bĭg| *adj.* Large; great in amount or size: *big mountain.* ***bigger, biggest***

bigger |bĭg′ər| *adj.* Larger; greater in amount or size: *a bigger piece of fruit.* [see *big*]

bind |bīnd| *v.* **1.** To fasten together between covers: *will bind these papers.* **2.** To fasten or tie together: *to bind with string or ribbon.* ***binds, bound, binding, binder***

birthday |bûrth′dā′| *n.* The day on which someone is born: *fourteenth birthday.* ***birthdays***

blade |blād| *n.* **1.** The metal part of an ice skate: *sharp blade on the new skate.* **2.** The flat, sharp part of an object used for cutting: *knife blade.* ***blades***

blame |blām| *n.* Responsibility, or duty, for something wrong: *took the blame. v.* To find fault: *will blame you for breaking the store window.* **blames, blamed, blaming, blameful, blameless**

blanket |blăng′kĭt| *n.* A woven covering used to keep people or animals warm: *a wool blanket.* **blankets, blanketed, blanketing**

blast |blăst| *n.* An explosion, or loud noise: *a blast from the mine.* **blasts, blasted, blasting**

blaze |blāz| *n.* A fire or a bright flame: *warmed by the blaze.* **blazes, blazed, blazing**

blind |blīnd| *adj.* Hidden; hard to see: *blind curve.* **blinds, blinded, blinding, blindly, blindness**

block |blŏk| *n.* Something hard and solid: *huge block of ice.* **blocks, blocked, blocking, blocker**

blocks |blŏks| *n.* More than one block: *blocks of bricks.* [see *block*]

bloom |blōōm| *v.* To have or open into flowers: *will bloom in April. n.* A flower or blossom: *a spring bloom.* **blooms, bloomed, blooming, bloomer**

board |bôrd| *n.* A long, flat piece of wood used in building: *a four-foot board.* **boards, boarded, boarding, boarder**

boil |boil| *v.* To bubble and give off steam due to heating: *will boil the soup.* **boils, boiled, boiling, boiler**

born |bôrn| *adj.* Brought into life: *born on December 5.*

bother |bŏth′ər| *v.* To trouble, annoy, or pester: *won't bother you with any noise.* **bothers, bothered, bothering**

bound |bound| *v.* Fastened together; tied: *bound with rope.* [see *bind*]

branch |brănch| *n.* A division of a main part: *a branch of the road.* **branches, branched, branching**

brave |brāv| *adj.* Not afraid: *the brave hero.* **braver, bravest, braves, braved, braving, bravely, braveness, bravery**

break |brāk| *v.* To take or come apart: *to break a dish.* **breaks, broke, broken, breaking, breaker**

breath |brĕth| *n.* The air that goes into and comes out of the lungs: *a deep breath.* **—Out of breath—**Breathless. **breaths, breather, breathless, breathlessly, breathlessness, breathe, breathes, breathed, breathing,**

brick |brĭk| *adj.* Made of bricks: *brick house. n.* A block of clay baked by sun or fire until hard: *built of brick.* **bricks, bricked, bricking**

broke |brōk| *v.* Took or came apart: *broke the dish.* [see *break*]

bruise |brōōz| *n.* An injury from a fall or blow that leaves a black-and-blue mark: *arm bruise.* **bruises, bruised, bruising**

brush |brŭsh| *v.* To clean, sweep, groom, or paint with a brush: *to brush your hair.* **brushes, brushed, brushing**

bucket |bŭk′ĭt| *n.* A round container used for carrying such things as water, sand, milk, or coal: *a bucket of sand.* **buckets**

---

build |bĭld| *v.* To make something by putting together materials or parts: *to build a house.* **builds, built, building, buildings, builder**

built |bĭlt| *v.* Made something by putting together materials or parts: *built a bookcase.* [see *build*]

bump |bŭmp| *n.* **1.** A small place that rises above what is around it: *a bump in the road.* **2.** A lump or swelling: *bump on his head.* **bumps, bumped, bumping, bumper, bumpy**

burn |bûrn| *v.* To set on fire: *to burn the pile of leaves. n.* An injury caused by fire or heat: *a burn from the hot pan.* **burns, burned, burnt, burning, burner**

busy |bĭz'ē| *adj.* Active; working; having plenty to do: *busy person.* **busier, busiest, busyness**

C

cabin |kăb'ĭn| *n.* A small, plain house: *cabin made of logs.* **cabins**

cable |kā'bəl| *n.* A strong, thick rope made of twisted wire: *to pull the heavy wagon with a cable.* —**Cable car**—A car pulled by an overhead cable. **cables, cabled**

camel |kăm'əl| *n.* A large four-footed animal with either one or two humps and a long neck, found in Africa and Asia: *a camel at the zoo.* **camels**

candle |kăn'dl| *n.* A stick of wax with a wick inside: *tall, thin candle.* **candles**

can't |kănt| Contraction for *cannot: can't go home.*

cape |kāp| *n.* A sleeveless coat that hangs loosely from the shoulders, fastened at the neck: *a winter cape.* **capes**

care |kâr| *n.* Attention or caution: *to iron the clothes with care.* **cares, cared, caring, careless, carelessly, carelessness, careful, carefully, carefulness**

careful |kâr'fəl| *adj.* Paying attention; cautious: *a careful driver.* [see *care*]

careless |kâr'lĭs| *adj.* Not paying attention: *was careless and fell.* [see *care*]

case |kās| *n.* A container to hold something: *a leather case.* **cases, cased, casing**

cases |kā'sĭz| *n.* More than one case: *wooden cases for toys.* [see *case*]

cash |kăsh| *v.* To get money for: *to cash a check. n.* Money in the form of bills and coins: *extra cash in the bank.* **cashes, cashed, cashing, cashier**

cattle |kăt'l| *n.* Cows, bulls, and steers raised for meat and milk: *herd of cattle.*

cent |sĕnt| *n.* A penny; a coin of the United States and Canada: *one cent.* **cents**

center |sĕn'tər| *n.* The middle part or place of something: *in the center of the table.* **centers, centered, centering, central**

cents |sĕnts| *n.* More than one penny: *two cents.* [see *cent*]

chain |chān| *n.* A row of rings joined together: *a gold chain.* **chains, chained, chaining**

chance |chăns| *n.* The possibility that something will happen: *a good chance of rain.* **chances, chanced, chancing**

change |chānj| *n.* **1.** A passing from one form or place to another: *a change of weather.* **2.** Money given back when a larger amount is paid than the price of what is bought: *ten cents in change. v.* To put something in place of another: *will change the sheets.* **changes, changed, changing, changeable**

chart |chärt| *n.* A table, diagram, graph, etc., that gives information: *a weather chart.* **charts, charted, charting**

chase |chās| *n.* The act of following after and trying to catch: *a long chase. v.* To follow in order to catch: *to chase them through the woods.* **chases, chased, chasing, chaser**

check |chĕk| *n.* A written order telling a bank to pay money to the person named: *paid by check.* **checks, checked, checking, checker**

cheer |chîr| *v.* **1.** To give a shout of happiness, support, or praise: *to cheer loudly at the game.* **2.** To make or become happier: *a gift to cheer you.* **cheers, cheered, cheering, cheerful, cheerfully, cheery, cheerier, cheeriest, cheeriness**

choose |chōōz| *v.* To pick from a group: *will choose another seat.* **chooses, chose, chosen, choosing, choosy, choosier, choosiest, choosiness, chooser**

chop |chŏp| *n.* A small piece of meat with a bone: *a pork chop. v.* To cut by hitting with a sharp tool: *will chop the carrots for dinner.* **chops, chopped, chopping, chopper**

chose |chōz| *v.* Picked from a group: *chose a book.* [see *choose*]

clever |klĕv'ər| *adj.* Showing quick thinking; skillful: *clever idea.* **cleverer, cleverest, cleverly, cleverness**

climb |klīm| *v.* To move upward using hands and feet: *can climb a tree like a monkey.* **climbs, climbed, climbing, climber**

cloth |klôth| *n.* A piece of woven material used in making clothes: *cotton cloth.* **cloths, clothe, clothes, clothed, clothing**

clothes |klōz| *n.* Things worn to cover the body: *bought new clothes.* [see *cloth*]

clothing |klō'thĭng| *adj.* Of or for clothing: *clothing brush. n.* Clothes: *warm winter clothing.* [see *cloth*]

clown |kloun| *n.* A person who makes people laugh: *a circus clown.* **clowns, clowned, clowning, clownish**

club |klŭb| *adj.* Of a club: *club trip. n.* A group of people meeting for a special purpose: *a club at school.* **clubs, clubbed, clubbing**

coach |kōch| *n.* A teacher or trainer of athletes and performers: *our team's coach.* **coaches, coached, coaching**

coal |kōl| *n.* A black mineral used for fuel: *heats with coal.* **coals**

coin |koin| *n.* A flat, round piece of metal used as money: *a silver coin.* **coins, coined, coining, coinage**

color |kŭl'ər| *n.* One of the parts of the spectrum; a certain shade, hue, or tint: *a bright color in the painting.* **colors, colored, coloring, colorful**

copy |kŏp'ē| *v.* To make something exactly like something else: *will copy this word. n.* Something made to look exactly like something else: *made a copy of the letter.* **copies, copied, copying, copier**

corner |kôr'nər| *n.* The place where two surfaces or lines meet: *corner of the room.* **corners, cornered, cornering**

ă pat / ā pay / â care / ä father / ĕ pet / ē be / ĭ pit / ī pie / î fierce / ŏ pot / ō go / ô paw, for / oi oil / ŏŏ book / ōō boot / ou out / ŭ cut / û fur / *th* the / th thin / hw which / zh vision / ə ago, item, pencil, atom, circus
©1977 by Houghton Mifflin Company. Reprinted by permission from THE AMERICAN HERITAGE SCHOOL DICTIONARY.

correct |kə rĕkt′| *adj.* Right; not having mistakes: *correct answer.* *v.* To mark the mistakes in: *will correct the test.* **corrects, corrected, correcting, correctly, correction, correctness**

count |kount| *v.* To find the total number of: *to count correctly.* **counts, counted, counting, counter**

crack |krăk| *n.* A narrow split or opening: *crack in the earth.* **cracks, cracked, cracking, cracker**

crash |krăsh| *v.* To fall, hit, or break suddenly with a loud noise: *will crash into the table.* *n.* A forceful fall, hit, or break with a loud noise: *the crash of dishes.* **crashes, crashed, crashing**

cried |krīd| *v.* Shed tears: *cried all night.* [see *cry*]

crime |krīm| *n.* An action against the law: *the crime of stealing.* **crimes, criminal**

cross |krôs| *v.* To draw a line across: *will cross a t.* **crosses, crossed, crossing,**

crossing |krô′sĭng| *v.* Drawing a line across: *crossing out mistakes.* [see *cross*]

crowd |kroud| *n.* A large number of people gathered together: *a crowd of students.* **crowds, crowded, crowding**

cry |krī| *v.* To shed tears: *to cry when sad.* **cries, cried, crying, crier**

D

dance |dăns| *v.* To move in time to music: *likes to dance fast.* **dances, danced, dancing, dancer**

dancing |dăn′sĭng| *v.* Moving in time to music: *dancing the waltz.* [see *dance*]

danger |dān′jər| *n.* The chance of something bad happening: *was full of danger.* **dangers, dangerous, dangerously**

dare |dâr| *v.* To have courage to try: *to dare to escape.* *n.* A challenge or contest: *a dare to jump.* **dares, dared, daring, daringly**

dash |dăsh| *n.* A fast run: *a dash for the door.* **dashes, dashed, dashing**

dawn |dôn| *n.* Daybreak; the time at which daylight first appears: *left before dawn.* **dawns, dawned, dawning**

death |dĕth| *n.* The end of living: *the bird's death.* **deaths, deathly**

December |dĭ sĕm′bər| *adj.* Of December: *December storm.* *n.* The last and twelfth month in the year: *the first week of December.* **Dec.**

deck |dĕk| *n.* **1.** A level on a ship: *the lower deck.* **2.** A set of playing cards: *shuffled the deck.* **decks, decked, decking**

deliver |dĭ lĭv′ər| *v.* To carry and hand out: *to deliver the mail.* **delivers, delivered, delivering, delivery, deliverer**

demand |dĭ mănd′| *v.* To ask for strongly: *to demand an answer.* **demands, demanded, demanding**

didn't |dĭd′nt| Contraction for *did not:* *didn't finish.*

dim |dĭm| *v.* To make less bright: *to dim the headlights.* *adj.* Having or giving little light; not bright: *dim moonlight.* **dims, dimmed, dimming, dimmer, dimmest, dimly, dimness**

dirt |dûrt| *n.* Dust, mud, or any material that makes something unclean: *dirt on his face.* **dirty, dirtier, dirtiest, dirties, dirtied, dirtying**

dirty |dûr′tē| *adj.* Unclean: *dirty hands.* [see *dirt*]

discover |dĭ skŭv′ər| *v.* To find out for the first time: *might discover buried treasure.* **discovers, discovered, discovering, discoverer, discovery**

dive |dīv| *n.* A headfirst plunge into water: *a dive into the pool.* **dives, dived, dove, diving, diver**

draft |drăft| *n.* A flow of air: *a cold draft from the broken window.* **drafts, drafted, drafting**

drag |drăg| *v.* To pull or move slowly and heavily: *to drag the heavy box.* **drags, dragged, dragging, dragger**

drain |drān| *v.* To draw off or flow off slowly: *will drain the liquid.* *n.* A pipe for carrying off water or waste: *a drain for the bathroom sink.* **drains, drained, draining**

drank |drăngk| *v.* Swallowed liquids: *drank a glass of milk.* [see *drink*]

draw |drô| *v.* To pull or take out: *to draw a winning number from the hat.* **draws, drew, drawn, drawing, drawings, drawer**

dream |drēm| *n.* The pictures and thoughts seen during sleep: *had a scary dream about monsters.* **dreams, dreamed, dreamt, dreaming, dreamy, dreamer**

drill |drĭl| *n.* A tool for making holes in hard material: *the electric drill.* **drills, drilled, drilling**

drink |drĭngk| *v.* To swallow liquids: *to drink slowly.* **drinks, drank, drunk, drinking**

drive |drīv| *v.* To control the movement of a car or other vehicle: *to drive to the store for groceries.* **drives, drove, driving, driver**

driving |drī′vĭng| *v.* Controlling the movement of a car or other vehicle: *was driving a truck.* [see *drive*]

during |dŏŏr′ĭng| *prep.* **1.** Through the entire time of: *during the storm.* **2.** At some point of time: *during the first hour.*

E

early |ûr′lē| *adv.* At or close to the beginning of a time period: *woke early in the morning.* **earlier, earliest**

earn |ûrn| *v.* To get paid for work done: *to earn twenty dollars.* **earns, earned, earning, earnings, earner**

earth |ûrth| *n.* The planet we live on: *circled the earth.* **earthy, earthen, earthly**

eleven |ĭ lĕv′ən| *n.* A number equal to one more than ten: *eleven plus two.* **elevens, eleventh**

enjoy |ĕn joi′| *v.* To be happy with; get joy and pleasure from: *to enjoy downhill skiing.* **enjoys, enjoyed, enjoying, enjoyable, enjoyably, enjoyment**

enter |ĕn′tər| *v.* **1.** To join; become a member of: *will enter the contest.* **2.** To go or come into: *to enter the room.* **enters, entered, entering, entrance**

evening |ēv′nĭng| *n.* The time between late afternoon and early nighttime: *five o'clock in the evening.* **evenings**

ă pat / ā pay / â care / ä father / ĕ pet / ē be / ĭ pit / ī pie / î fierce / ŏ pot / ō go / ô paw, for / oi oil / ŏŏ book / ŏŏ boot / ou out / ŭ cut / û fur / *th* the / th thin / hw which / zh vision / ə ago, item, pencil, atom, circus

event |ĭ vĕnt′| *n.* One of the contests in a program of sports: *the final event.* **events, eventful, eventfully**

everybody |ĕv′rē bŏd′ē| *pron.* All people: *everybody here.*

everyone |ĕv′rē wŭn′| *pron.* Everybody: *everyone in the room.*

everything |ĕv′rē thĭng′| *pron.* All things: *everything you brought.*

F

fade |fād| *v.* To dim; lose color: *will fade in the sun.* **fades, faded, fading**

fall |fôl| *v.* To drop from a higher place: *to fall from a ladder.* **falls, fell, falling, fallen**

fallen |fô′lən| *adj.* Down on the ground: *fallen leaves.* [see *fall*]

far |fär| *adv.* To or at a great distance: *far from home.* **farther, farthest**

farther |fär′thər| *adv.* To or at a greater distance: *farther from shore.* [see *far*]

fate |fāt| *n.* **1.** What happens to a person or thing: *the fate of snow on a warm day.* **2.** The power believed to control what will happen: *caused by fate.* **fates, fated, fateful**

fear |fîr| *v.* To feel afraid or that danger, pain, or the unknown is near: *does fear the dark.* **fears, feared, fearing, fearful, fearfully, fearfulness, fearless, fearlessly, fearlessness**

fears |fîrz| *v.* Feels afraid or that danger, pain, or the unknown is near: *fears large animals.* [see *fear*]

feast |fēst| *n.* A large meal prepared for a special occasion: *cooked for the king's feast.* **feasts, feasted, feasting**

February |fĕb′rōō ĕr′ē| *n.* The second month in the year: *not until February.* **Feb.**

feel |fēl| *v.* To have the sense of being: *to feel sad.* **feels, felt, feeling, feelings, feeler**

feeling |fē′lĭng| *v.* Having the sense of being: *feeling warm.* [see *feel*]

fence |fĕns| *n.* A railing or wall used to protect or mark off an area: *a wooden fence around the yard.* **fences, fenced, fencing, fencer**

fever |fē′vər| *n.* A body temperature higher than usual: *sick with a fever.* **fevers, feverish**

few |fyōō| *adj.* Not many: *a few people.* **fewer, fewest**

field |fēld| *n.* An open land with few or no trees: *ran across the field behind the school.* **fields**

film |fĭlm| *n.* A motion picture; movie: *went to see the new film.* **films, filmed, filming, filmy**

fireplace |fīr′plās′| *n.* An opening in a room for holding a fire: *burned in the fireplace.* **fireplaces**

flash |flăsh| *n.* **1.** A sudden, short blast of light: *a flash of lightning.* **2.** An instant; a split second: *happened in a flash.* **flashes, flashed, flashing, flasher, flashy**

fled |flĕd| *v.* Ran away from: *fled the fire.* [see *flee*]

flee |flē| *v.* To run away from: *to flee danger.* **flees, fled, fleeing**

flock |flŏk| *n.* A group of one kind of animal: *a flock of geese.* **flocks, flocked, flocking**

floor |flôr| *n.* **1.** The part of a room that a person stands or walks on: *a wooden floor.* **2.** A level, or story, of a building: *lives on the second floor.* **floors**

flour |flour| *n.* A fine powder made by grinding grains: *measured flour for the vanilla cake.* **flours, floured, flouring, floury**

flow |flō| *n.* Any steady, smooth movement: *the flow of the water.* **flows, flowed, flowing**

follow |fŏl′ō| *v.* To go or come after: *to follow the leader.* **follows, followed, following, follower**

fond |fŏnd| *adj.* Loving or liking: *a fond hug.* —**Fond of**—Having a liking for. **fonder, fondest, fondly, fondness**

fork |fôrk| *n.* **1.** One of the parts into which something divides: *the left fork in the road.* **2.** An eating tool with a handle at one end and pointed parts at the other: *a fork and a spoon.* **forks, forked, forking**

fort |fôrt| *n.* A building or area that soldiers protect against an enemy: *the army's fort.* **forts, fortress, fortify**

forty |fôr′tē| *adj.* Four times ten: *forty pennies.* **forties, fortieth**

four |fôr| *adj.* One more than three: *four oranges.* **fours, fourth, fourths**

fourteen |fôr′tēn′| *adj.* Four more than ten: *fourteen students.* **fourteens, fourteenth**

fourth |fôrth| *adj.* Next after the third: *fourth grade.* [see *four*]

frame |frām| *n.* A form that borders something: *the window frame.* **frames, framed, framing, framer**

freeze |frēz| *v.* To harden into a solid by cold: *to freeze water into ice.* **freezes, froze, frozen, freezing, freezer**

fresh |frĕsh| *adj.* Just made or grown: *fresh bread.* **fresher, freshest, freshly, freshness**

Friday |frī′dā′| *adj.* Of Friday: *Friday cookout. n.* The sixth day of the week: *every Friday.* **Fri.**

fried |frīd| *adj.* Cooked in fat: *a pan of fried potatoes.* [see *fry*]

friend |frĕnd| *n.* A person someone knows and likes: *my good friend.* **friends, friendly, friendlier, friendliest**

friends |frĕndz| *n.* More than one friend: *his friends at school.* [see *friend*]

front |frŭnt| *adj.* At or near the forward part: *on the front page. n.* The part that comes first or faces forward: *the front of the room.* **fronts**

froze |frōz| *v.* Became hardened by cold: *when the pond froze.* [see *freeze*]

fry |frī| *v.* To cook in fat: *to fry eggs.* **fries, fried, frying, fryer**

 G

gang |găng| *n.* A group of people who work or play together: *a gang of friends. v.* To form into a group: *to gang together for the trip.* —**Gang up on**—To attack as a group. **gangs, ganged, ganging**

ă pat / ā pay / â care / ä father / ĕ pet / ē be / ĭ pit / ī pie / î fierce / ŏ pot / ō go / ô paw, for / oi oil / o͝o book /
o͞o boot / ou out / ŭ cut / û fur / *th* the / th thin / hw which / zh vision / ə ago, item, pencil, atom, circus

get |gĕt| *v.* To be or become: *to get warmer.* **gets, got, gotten, getting**

glass |glăs| *n.* A hard material that breaks easily and can be seen through: *broken glass.* **glasses, glassy, glassful**

glasses |glăs′ĭz| *n.* A pair of glass lenses worn to help a person see better: *glasses with gold frames.* [see *glass*]

globe |glōb| *n.* A world map in the shape of a ball: *the globe in our classroom.* **globes, global**

glow |glō| *n.* A light made by a fire, star, electricity, etc.: *the glow from the bulb.* **glows, glowed, glowing**

gold |gōld| *n.* A bright-yellow color: *red, blue, and gold.* **golds, golden**

golden |gōl′dən| *adj.* Bright-yellow: *long golden hair.* [see *gold*]

gotten |gŏt′n| *v.* Become: *had gotten tired.* [see *get*]

gown |goun| *n.* A long dress: *a new gown for the party.* **gowns**

grandmother |grănd′mŭ*th*′ər| *n.* The mother of one's father or mother: *visited my grandmother.* **grandmothers**

greet |grēt| *v.* To welcome in a friendly way: *to greet the guests.* **greets, greeted, greeting, greeter**

grind |grīnd| *v.* To crush into small pieces or powder: *to grind into flour.* **grinds, ground, grinding, grinder**

grip |grĭp| *n.* A tight hold or grasp: *a grip on the rope.* **grips, gripped, gripping**

grow |grō| *v.* **1.** To become: *to grow dark.* **2.** To cause to become bigger; raise: *to grow vegetables.* **grows, grew, grown, growing, growth**

grown |grōn| *v.* **1.** Become: *had grown very tall.* **2.** Caused to become bigger; raised: *had grown corn.* [see *grow*]

H

habit |hăb′ĭt| *n.* An action repeated over and over: *a habit of going to sleep early.* **habits**

hammer |hăm′ər| *n.* A tool with a metal head at the end of a long handle, used for driving nails: *a hammer and a saw.* **hammers, hammered, hammering**

handle |hăn′dl| *n.* The part of an object that is grasped or held by the hand: *the handle of the shovel.* **handles, handled, handling, handler**

handy |hăn′dē| *adj.* Easy to reach: *the handy bookshelf.* **handier, handiest, handily, handiness**

hang |hăng| *v.* To fasten to something above: *to hang your coat on the hook.* **hangs, hanged, hung, hanging, hanger**

happen |hăp′ən| *v.* To take place; occur: *to happen to us.* **happens, happened, happening**

happening |hăp′ə nĭng| *v.* Taking place; occurring: *happening tomorrow night.* [see *happen*]

harm |härm| *n.* Damage or injury: *caused harm to the forests.* *v.* To cause damage or injury to; hurt: *could harm you.* **harms, harmed, harming, harmful, harmless, harmlessness**

hate |hāt| *v.* To dislike very much: *to hate spiders.* **hates, hated, hating, hateful, hatefully**

hear |hîr| v. To take in sounds through the ear: *to hear the loud music.* **hears, heard, hearing**

heard |hûrd| v. Took in sounds through the ear: *heard the dog barking.* [see *hear*]

heart |härt| n. A red shape with rounded sides meeting in a point at the bottom and forming two curves at the top: *drew a red heart.* **hearts, hearty, heartier, heartiest**

heat |hēt| v. To make or become warm: *will heat our dinner.* **heats, heated, heating, heater**

heating |hē'tĭng| v. Making or becoming warm: *heating the milk.* [see *heat*]

heel |hēl| n. The piece of a shoe or boot under the back part of the foot: *a new heel for the shoe.* **heels, heeled, heeling**

hero |hîr'ō| n. A person noted and admired for courage, bravery, etc.: *a hero in battle.* **heroes, heroic, heroism**

he's |hēz| Contraction for *he is: if he's waiting.*

high |hī| adj. Tall: *a high mountain.* **higher, highest, highly, highness**

higher |hī'ər| adj. Taller: *higher kite.* [see *high*]

highest |hī'ĭst| adj. Tallest: *the highest building.* [see *high*]

highway |hī'wā'| n. A main road: *a two-lane highway.* **highways**

hire |hīr| v. To pay for work: *will hire two painters.* **hires, hired, hiring**

history |hĭs'tə rē| n. A record of past events: *the history of Europe.* adj. Of history: *a history test.* **histories, historic, historical, historian**

hold |hōld| v. To take and keep in one's hands: *to hold the books.* —**Hold off**— To delay or wait. **holds, held, holding, holdings, holder**

holding |hōl'dĭng| v. Taking and keeping in one's hands: *holding two packages.* [see *hold*]

hole |hōl| n. 1. An opening: *hole in my shirt.* 2. A hollow place in something solid: *dug a hole.* **holes, holey**

holes |hōlz| n. 1. Openings: *holes in the cloth.* 2. Hollow places: *two holes in the wall.* [see *hole*]

homesick |hōm'sĭk'| adj. Sad because of being away from home: *a homesick traveler.* **homesickness**

honey |hŭn'ē| n. A sweet liquid made by bees: *a spoonful of honey.* **honeys, honeyed**

hope |hōp| v. To wish: *does hope to get a new sweater.* **hopes, hoped, hoping, hopeful, hopefully, hopefulness, hopeless, hopelessly, hopelessness**

hoping |hō'pĭng| v. Wishing: *hoping to win.* [see *hope*]

hotel |hō tĕl'| n. A building that provides rooms and food for pay: *a room at the hotel.* **hotels**

hour |our| n. A period of time equal to 60 minutes: *waited for an hour.* **hours, hourly, hr.**

ă pat / ā pay / â care / ä father / ĕ pet / ē be / ĭ pit / ī pie / î fierce / ŏ pot / ō go / ô paw, for / oi oil / oŏ book /
oō boot / ou out / ŭ cut / û fur / *th* the / th thin / hw which / zh vision / ə ago, item, pencil, atom, circus
©1977 by Houghton Mifflin Company. Reprinted by permission from THE AMERICAN HERITAGE SCHOOL DICTIONARY.

huge |hyōoj| *adj.* Very big: *a huge canyon.* **huger, hugest, hugely, hugeness**

hundred |hŭn'drĭd| *n.* Ten times ten: *one hundred.* **hundreds, hundredth**

hung |hŭng| *v.* Fastened to something above: *hung my coat.* [see *hang*]

hunger |hŭng'gər| *n.* The desire, or want, for food: *a hunger for vegetables.* **hungers, hungered, hungering, hungry, hungrier, hungriest, hungrily, hungriness**

hungry |hŭng'grē| *adj.* Desiring, or wanting, food: *was not very hungry.* [see *hunger*]

hunt |hŭnt| *v.* To search or look for: *to hunt buried treasure.* **hunts, hunted, hunting, hunter, hunters**

hunter |hŭn'tər| *n.* A person who hunts or searches for something: *a hunter in the hills.* [see *hunt*]

I

inch |ĭnch| *n.* A measure of length equal to one twelfth of a foot: *one inch of snow.* **inches, inched, inching, in.**

inches |ĭnch'ĭz| *n.* More than one inch: *sixty inches tall.* [see *inch*]

indeed |ĭn dēd'| *adv.* In fact; really; truly: *is indeed pleased.*

iron |ī'ərn| *v.* To press clothes with a heated iron: *to iron the shirt.* *n.* A household tool with a flat bottom which is heated and used to press clothes: *unplugged the iron.* **irons, ironed, ironing**

island |ī'lənd| *n.* A piece of land surrounded by water: *sailed to the island.* **islands, islander**

it's |ĭts| Contraction for *it is: since it's cold outside.*

itself |ĭt sĕlf'| *pron.* A form used in place of *it*, often to show importance: *the monkey itself.*

J

jail |jāl| *n.* A building where people who have broken the law are kept: *the county jail.* **jails, jailed, jailing, jailer**

January |jăn'yōo ĕr'ē| *adj.* Of January: *a January vacation. n.* The first month in the year: *a birthday in January.* **Jan.**

jar |jär| *n.* A glass or clay container with a wide mouth: *a jar of jelly.* **jars, jarred, jarring**

job |jŏb| *n.* Work that has to be done: *his job to wash the dishes.* **jobs**

join |join| *v.* To meet: *to join our friends.* **joins, joined, joining, joiner**

July |jōo'lī'| *n.* The seventh month in the year: *going swimming in July.*

June |jōon| *n.* The sixth month in the year: *the last day in June.*

K

keep |kēp| *v.* **1.** To continue in a certain place or condition: *to keep together.* **2.** To have or hold for a long time: *will keep this picture.* **keeps, kept, keeping, keeper**

kept |kĕpt| *v.* **1.** Continued in a certain place or condition: *kept quiet.* **2.** Had or held for a long time: *kept the ring in a safe place.* [see *keep*]

kick |kĭk| *n.* A blow with the foot: *a swift kick.* *v.* To move something by striking with the foot, or kicking: *will kick the ball.* **kicks, kicked, kicking, kicker**

knee |nē| *n.* The joint where the thigh and lower leg meet: *fell on my knee.* **knees, kneel, kneels, knelt, kneeled, kneeling**

knew |noō| *v.* **1.** Skilled in: *knew how to type.* **2.** Was sure of the facts: *knew the answer.* [see *know*]

knife |nīf| *n.* A sharp tool used for cutting: *sliced with a knife.* **knifes, knifed, knifing, knives**

knot |nŏt| *n.* A fastening made by tying together pieces of rope or string: *a knot in my shoelace.* **knots, knotted, knotting, knotty**

know |nō| *v.* **1.** To have skill in: *to know how to dance.* **2.** To be sure of the facts: *to know the exact date.* **knows, knew, known, knowing, knowingly, knowledge**

knows |nōz| *v.* **1.** Has skill in: *knows how to sing.* **2.** Is sure of the facts: *knows where you live.* [see *know*]

L

lace |lās| *adj.* Made of lace: *lace curtains.* *n.* Fine threads woven in an open pattern: *trimmed with lace.* *v.* To fasten or tie with a string: *will lace my shoes.* **laces, laced, lacing, lacy**

ladder |lăd'ər| *n.* A piece of equipment used for climbing: *up the ladder.* **ladders**

lamb |lăm| *n.* A young sheep: *a sleeping lamb.* **lambs**

land |lănd| *n.* The surface of the earth not covered by water: *saw land from afar.* **lands, landed, landing, landings**

landing |lăn'dĭng| *n.* **1.** The platform between a set of stairs: *stopped on the landing.* **2.** A wharf or pier: *swam to the landing.* [see *land*]

late |lāt| *adv.* After the proper time: *arrived late.* **lately, later, latest, lateness**

lately |lāt'lē| *adv.* Not long ago: *have seen him lately.* [see *late*]

laugh |lăf| *v.* To make sounds that show happiness or enjoyment: *to laugh at the clown.* **laughs, laughed, laughing, laughable, laughter**

law |lô| *n.* A rule that must be followed: *obeys the law.* **laws, lawful, lawless, lawyer**

lawn |lôn| *n.* An area of grass around a house or building: *will mow the front lawn.* **—Lawn mower—**A machine for cutting grass. **lawns**

laws |lôz| *n.* More than one law: *broke no laws.* [see *law*]

lazy |lā'zē| *adj.* Not wanting to work or be active: *am lazy in the summer.* **lazier, laziest, lazily, laziness**

lead |lēd| *v.* To go to or be at the head of: *to lead the band.* **leads, led, leading, leader**

leading |lē'dĭng| *v.* Going to or being at the head of: *leading the race.* [see *lead*]

ă pat / ā pay / â care / ä father / ĕ pet / ē be / ĭ pit / ī pie / î fierce / ŏ pot / ō go / ô paw, for / oi oil / oŏ book / oō boot / ou out / ŭ cut / û fur / *th* the / th thin / hw which / zh vision / ə ago, item, pencil, atom, circus

leaf |lĕf| *n.* One of the thin, flat parts of a plant: *a leaf on the tree.* ***leaves, leafy***

leak |lĕk| *n.* A hole that lets something in or out by accident: *the tire with the leak.* ***leaks, leaked, leaking, leaky***

lean |lēn| *v.* To rest on a person or thing for support: *to lean against the wall.* ***leans, leaned, leaning, leaner, leanest***

leave |lĕv| *v.* To go away: *to leave at noon.* ***leaves, left, leaving***

leaving |lē′vĭng| *v.* Going away: *leaving tomorrow.* [see *leave*]

led |lĕd| *v.* Showed or guided: *led the flock of sheep.* [see *lead*]

lend |lĕnd| v. To let someone have or use for a time: *will lend you a sweater.* ***lends, lent, lending, lender***

less |lĕs| *pron.* Fewer things or people: *has less than you do. adj.* Not a large amount of: *have less homework.* **—Much less—** Especially not. [see *little*]

lesson |lĕs′ən| *n.* Something that is learned or taught: *a spelling lesson.* ***lessons***

let |lĕt| *v.* To allow: *to let him go.* ***lets, letting***

letting |lĕt′ĭng| *v.* Allowing: *letting him speak.* [see *let*]

level |lĕv′əl| *adj.* At an equal height: *level with the dining table.* ***levels, leveled, leveling, levelness***

lie |lī| *v.* To tell something that is not true: *to lie about where you went.* ***lies, lied, lying, liar***

light |līt| *adj.* Having little weight; not heavy: *a light box.* ***lights, lighted, lit, lighting, lightly, lighter, lightest, lightness***

lightly |līt′lē| *adv.* With little force or weight; softly: *floating lightly on air.* [see *light*]

lightning |līt′nĭng| *n.* A bright flash of light in the sky: *thunder and lightning.*

like |līk| *v.* To be pleased with: *to like our new neighbors.* ***likes, liked, liking, likely, likelier, likeliest, likeness***

likely |līk′lē| *adj.* To be expected: *likely to be cold.* [see *like*]

little |lĭt′l| *adj.* Small; not big or large; not much: *little time to talk.* ***littler, littlest, less, lesser, least, lessen, lessens, lessened, lessening***

live |lĭv| *v.* To make a home: *to live on Main Street.* ***lives, lived, living***

living |lĭv′ĭng| *v.* Making a home: *living in the city.* [see *live*]

load |lōd| *n.* A thing to carry: *a load of sand.* ***loads, loaded, loading, loader***

loads |lōdz| *n.* More than one load: *two loads of hay.* [see *load*]

lock |lŏk| *v.* To close with a lock: *will lock the front door.* ***unlock, unlocks, unlocked, unlocking***

loop |lo͞op| *n.* The rounded shape formed when a piece of rope or string crosses itself: *made a loop with ribbon.* ***loops, looped, looping***

loud |loud| *adj.* Not quiet: *a loud bang from the cannon.* ***louder, loudest, loudly, loudness***

luck |lŭk| *n.* Good fortune: *will wish you luck in the race.* ***lucky, luckier, luckiest, luckily***

lucky |lŭk′ē| *adj.* Having or bringing good fortune: *a lucky penny.* [see *luck*]

lump |lŭmp| *n.* **1.** A shapeless mass: *a lump of dough.* **2.** A bump or swelling: *a lump on my hand.* **lumps, lumped, lumping, lumpy, lumpiness**

lung |lŭng| *adj.* Of the lung: *lung operation.* *n.* One of two organs for breathing air: *left lung.* **lungs**

lying |lī′ĭng| *v.* Telling an untruth: *lying about the accident. adj.* Not telling the truth: *the lying thief.* [see *lie*]

M

mad |măd| *adj.* **1.** Very excited; foolish: *mad actions.* **2.** Angry: *mad for not winning.* **madder, maddest, madden, maddens, maddened, maddening, madly, madness**

madder |măd′ər| *adj.* Angrier: *madder than yesterday.* [see *mad*]

madly |măd′lē| *adv.* With great energy or power: *is working madly.* [see *mad*]

magic |măj′ĭk| *adj.* Done by using tricks to make things that seem impossible happen: *a magic wand.* **magical, magically, magician**

mail |māl| *n.* The system by which letters and packages are sent: *delivered by mail.* **mails, mailed, mailing, mailer**

mailed |māld| *v.* Sent by mail: *mailed the package.* [see *mail*]

make |māk| *v.* To put together: *to make a salad.* **makes, made, making**

making |mā′kĭng| *v.* Putting together: *making new clothes.* [see *make*]

map |măp| *v.* To make a map, or chart, that shows where things are located: *will map the city streets.* **maps, mapped, mapping**

mapping |măp′ĭng| *v.* To make a map of: *was mapping the stars in the sky.* [see *map*]

marble |mär′bəl| *adj.* Made of marble: *a marble tabletop. n.* A hard, polished round stone or glass: *a brightly colored marble.* **marbles, marbled, marbling**

March |märch| *n.* The third month in the year: *a birthday in March.* **Mar.**

mark |märk| *n.* A spot made on one object by another: *left a mark on the floor. v.* To show clearly: *will mark my place with this paper.* **marks, marked, marking, marker**

marker |mär′kər| *n.* **1.** Something used to draw or write: *paper and a blue marker.* **2.** A piece of paper, cloth, leather, etc., used to hold, or mark, one's place in a book: *found the marker on page 280.* [see *mark*]

mask |măsk| *n.* A covering that hides or protects the face: *a frightful mask.* **masks, masked, masking**

matter |măt′ər| *v.* To be important: *won't matter if we lose.* **matters, mattered**

May |mā| *n.* The fifth month in the year: *the first day of May.*

meal |mēl| *n.* Food served and eaten at one time: *a meal of meat and potatoes.* **meals**

ă pat / ā pay / â care / ä father / ĕ pet / ē be / ĭ pit / ī pie / î fierce / ŏ pot / ō go / ô paw, for / oi oil / ŏŏ book /
ōō boot / ou out / ŭ cut / û fur / th the / th thin / hw which / zh vision / ə ago, item, pencil, atom, circus
©1977 by Houghton Mifflin Company. Reprinted by permission from THE AMERICAN HERITAGE SCHOOL DICTIONARY.

mean |mēn| v. To intend; have as a purpose: *to mean something by her comment.* **means, meant, meaning, meaner, meanest, meaningful**

means |mēnz| v. Intends; has as a purpose: *means to do well.* [see *mean*]

meet |mēt| v. To come together by appointment: *to meet at four o'clock.* **meets, met, meeting**

meeting |mē'tĭng| n. A coming together: *a business meeting.* [see *meet*]

melt |mĕlt| v. To turn into a liquid by heating: *to melt wax.* **melts, melted, melting**

middle |mĭd'l| n. The point equally distant between two sides or times; center: *middle of the room.*

might |mīt| n. Great power, strength, or skill: *the might of the storm.* **mighty, mightier, mightiest**

mighty |mī'tē| adj. Powerful, strong, or skillful: *a mighty lion.* [see *might*]

mild |mīld| adj. Not very hot or cold: *a mild winter.* **milder, mildest, mildly, mildness**

mile |mīl| n. A measure of distance equal to 5,280 feet: *drove for one mile.* **miles, mileage**

mint |mĭnt| n. A plant used for flavoring: *lemonade with mint.* **mints, minted, minting, minty**

mist |mĭst| n. Very fine drops of water in the air: *mist on the windshield.* **mists, misted, misting, misty**

mix |mĭks| v. To combine together by stirring: *to mix flour, water, and eggs.* **mixes, mixed, mixing, mixer, mixture**

Monday |mŭn'dā'| n. The second day of the week: *starts school on Monday.* **Mon.**

monster |mŏn'stər| n. An imaginary creature that is very large and frightening: *saw an ugly monster.* **monsters, monstrous, monstrosity**

month |mŭnth| n. One of twelve periods of time in a year: *the month of January.* **months, monthly**

mostly |mōst'lē| adv. Mainly; for the most part: *mostly cloudy.* [see *much*]

mouse |mous| n. A small furry animal with a long tail: *a gray mouse.* **mice, mousy**

much |mŭch| adv. Greatly: *not much pleased with the painting.* **more, most, mostly**

music |myōō'zĭk| n. An interesting or pleasing combination of sounds: *loud music.* **musical, musically, musician**

N

nail |nāl| n. A thin, pointed piece of metal used to hold things together: *will hammer the nail.* **nails, nailed, nailing**

nails |nālz| n. More than one nail: *tools and nails.* [see *nail*]

near |nîr| adj. Close by in space or time: *in the near future.* **nears, neared, nearing, nearer, nearest, nearness, nearly**

nearest |nîr'ĭst| adj. Closest: *the nearest exit.* [see *near*]

nineteen |nīn'tĕn'| adj. Nine more than ten: *nineteen people.* n. Nine more than ten: *a group of nineteen.* **nineteens, nineteenth**

nobody |nō′bŏd′ē| *pron.* No person: *nobody allowed inside.*

noise |noiz| *n.* A loud and unpleasant sound: *too much noise.* **noises, noisy, noisier, noisiest, noisily, noisiness**

none |nŭn| *pron.* Not any: *have none left.*

notebook |nōt′bŏŏk′| *n.* A book with blank pages on which to write: *wrote a poem in my notebook.* **notebooks**

notebooks |nōt′bŏŏks′| *n.* More than one notebook: *bought two notebooks for school.* [see *notebook*]

November |nō věm′bər| *n.* The eleventh month in the year: *took a vacation in November.* **Nov.**

number |nŭm′bər| *n.* **1.** A numeral connected with a person or thing: *telephone number.* **2.** A numeral: *the next number.* **numbers, numbered, numbering**

nurse |nûrs| *n.* A person trained to take care of people who are sick: *the doctor and the nurse.* **nurses, nursed, nursing, nursery**

O

oak |ōk| *adj.* Made of wood from an oak tree: *an oak floor.* *n.* **1.** A tree with strong wood and acorns: *the oak in the yard.* **2.** The wood from an oak tree: *a chair of oak.* **oaks**

ocean |ō′shən| *n.* One of the large bodies of salt water that covers almost all of the earth's surface: *swam in the ocean.* **oceans**

o'clock |ə klŏk′| *adv.* According to the clock: *begins at two o'clock.*

October |ŏk tō′bər| *adj.* Of October: *an October holiday. n.* The tenth month in the year: *a day in October.* **Oct.**

oil |oil| *n.* A greasy substance that does not mix with water: *a can of oil.* **oils, oiled, oiling, oily**

old |ōld| *adj.* Not young: *an old tree.* **older, oldest**

oldest |ōl′dĭst| *adj.* Having lived for the longest time: *oldest brother.* [see *old*]

omit |ō mĭt′| *v.* To leave out: *to omit the salt.* **omits, omitted, omitting**

only |ōn′lē| *adj.* By itself; one and no more: *the only window.*

open |ō′pən| *v.* To make or become not shut: *to open the door.* **opens, opened, opening, openings, openly, opener**

opening |ō′pə nĭng| *n.* A hole: *covered the opening.* [see *open*]

orange |ôr′ĭnj| *n.* A reddish-yellow citrus fruit: *ate an orange.* **oranges**

ounce |ouns| *n.* A measure of weight equal to one sixteenth of a pound: *one ounce of cheese.* **ounces, oz.**

outfit |out′fĭt′| *n.* All the articles or clothing necessary for a special purpose: *a skiing outfit.* **outfits, outfitted, outfitting, outfitter**

ă pat / ā pay / â care / ä father / ĕ pet / ē be / ĭ pit / ī pie / î fierce / ŏ pot / ō go / ô paw, for / oi oil / ŏŏ book / ōō boot / ou out / ŭ cut / û fur / *th* the / th thin / hw which / zh vision / ə ago, item, pencil, atom, circus

outfits |out′fĭts′| *n.* More than one outfit: *outfits for hiking.* [see *outfit*]

own |ōn| *v.* To have: *does own a bicycle.* **owns, owned, owning, owner, owners**

owner |ō′nər| *n.* A person who owns: *owner of the lost cat.* [see *own*]

P

pack |păk| *v.* To fill with items: *to pack a suitcase.* **packs, packed, packing, packer**

package |păk′ĭj| *n.* A group of items packed or wrapped together: *mailed a package.* **packages, packaged, packaging**

packed |păkt| *v.* Filled with items: *packed the box.* [see *pack*]

paddle |păd′l| *v.* To move a boat with a short oar: *to paddle across the lake. n.* A piece of wood with a handle at one end, used for mixing, stirring, etc.: *a paddle for stirring cement.* **paddles, paddled, paddling, paddler**

pain |pān| *n.* A feeling of hurt caused by an injury or sickness: *felt a sudden and sharp pain.* **pains, painful, painfully, painfulness, painless, painlessly, painlessness**

part |pärt| *n.* Not all: *part of the problem.* **parts, parted, parting, partner, partly**

partly |pärt′lē| *adv.* In part; in some measure or degree: *partly to blame.* [see *part*]

party |pär′tē| *n.* A group of people gathered together to have fun: *played games at the party.* **parties, partied, partying**

paste |pāst| *n.* A thick mixture used to stick things together: *has used paste to put photos in the album.* **pastes, pasted, pasting, pasty**

peek |pēk| *v.* To look at secretly: *to peek into the room.* **peeks, peeked, peeking**

phone |fōn| *n.* An instrument for sending and receiving speech over long distances; a telephone: *talked on the phone.* **phones, phoned, phoning**

picnic |pĭk′nĭk| *adj.* Of or for a picnic: *picnic lunch. n.* A meal that is eaten outside: *made salad for the picnic.* **picnics, picnicked, picnicking, picnicker**

picture |pĭk′chər| *n.* A drawing, painting, or photograph of someone or something: *a picture of my family.* **pictures, pictured, picturing**

pile |pīl| *n.* A large amount of things stacked on top of each other: *a pile of clothes.* **piles, piled, piling**

pillow |pĭl′ō| *n.* A stuffed cloth case that is used to support a person's head while lying down: *a pillow on the bed.* **pillows**

plane |plān| *n.* A machine with propellers or jet engines that make it fly; an airplane: *landed the plane.* **planes**

playmate |plā′māt′| *n.* A person who plays with someone else: *playmate in the neighborhood.* **playmates**

plenty |plĕn′tē| *n.* A full supply of all that is needed: *plenty of water.* **plentiful, plentifully**

plum |plŭm| *n.* A juicy purple fruit with a smooth skin and a pit: *a plum and a pear.* **plums**

pocket |pŏk′ĭt| *n.* A small bag for holding things, sewn into clothing: *keys in her pocket.* **pockets, pocketed, pocketing, pocketful**

poem |pō′əm| *n.* A form of writing with words arranged in verses that often rhyme: *a poem about summer.* **poems, poet, poetry**

point |point| *n.* The main purpose or idea: *understood the point you made.* **points, pointed, pointing, pointless, pointer**

pool |pо͞ol| *n.* A tank of water for swimming: *swam to the edge of the pool.* **pools**

porch |pôrch| *n.* A covered area built onto a house: *on the front porch.* **porches**

post |pōst| *n.* A straight piece of wood or metal used to hold something up: *nailed to the post.* **posts, posted, posting**

poster |pō′stər| *n.* A large printed notice put out for the public to see: *a circus poster.* **posters**

pound |pound| *n.* A unit of weight equal to sixteen ounces: *one pound of fish.* **pounds, pounded, pounding, lb.**

pour |pôr| *v.* To flow or cause to flow steadily: *to pour milk.* **pours, poured, pouring**

pouring |pôr′ĭng| *v.* Flowing or causing to flow steadily: *pouring from the hose.* *adj.* Flowing: *pouring rain.* [see *pour*]

power |pou′ər| *adj.* Run by a motor: *a power drill. n.* Strength: *the power of five people.* **powers, powered, powering, powerful, powerfully**

press |prĕs| *n.* A machine for printing books, magazines, and newspapers: *operated the press. v.* To put force on something: *to press the door shut.* **presses, pressed, pressing**

pretend |prĭ tĕnd′| *v.* To make believe: *to pretend you are flying.* **pretends, pretended, pretending, pretender**

price |prīs| *n.* The cost or amount of money for which something is bought or sold: *for the same price.* **prices, priced, pricing**

prices |prī′sĭz| *n.* Costs: *low prices for gas.* [see *price*]

pride |prīd| *n.* Pleasure in one's actions or worth; self-respect: *takes pride in her schoolwork.* **prides, prided, priding, prideful**

print |prĭnt| *n.* Letters in ink, stamped by type: *easy-to-read print. v.* To write in block letters, like those seen in print: *will print my name.* **prints, printed, printing, printer**

prize |prīz| *n.* An award won in a contest or game: *tried to win the prize.* **prizes, prized, prizing**

proud |proud| *adj.* Feeling very pleased or satisfied: *a proud winner.* **prouder, proudest, proudly**

provide |prə vīd′| *v.* **1.** To prepare ahead of time: *to provide lunch and dinner.* **2.** To give what is needed: *will provide pens and paper.* **provides, provided, providing, provider**

purse |pûrs| *n.* A handbag or pocketbook: *a leather purse.* **purses**

ă pat / ā pay / â care / ä father / ĕ pet / ē be / ĭ pit / ī pie / î fierce / ŏ pot / ō go / ô paw, for / oi oil / о͞o book / о͞o boot / ou out / ŭ cut / û fur / th the / th thin / hw which / zh vision / ə ago, item, pencil, atom, circus

Q

queen |kwēn| n. A female monarch, or ruler; a king's wife: *the queen on her throne.* **queens, queenly**

quiet |**kwī′ĭt**| adj. Peaceful; with little noise: *a quiet time.* **quieter, quietest, quietly, quietness**

quit |kwĭt| v. **1.** To give up: *to quit the team.* **2.** To stop: *will quit painting my room before noon.* **quits, quitted, quitting, quitter**

quite |kwīt| adv. Completely: *quite clear.*

R

race |rās| n. A contest to find the fastest: *an automobile race.* **races, raced, racing, racer**

races |**rā′sĭz**| n. More than one race: *bicycle races.* [see *race*]

rack |răk| n. A bar or stand on which to hang things: *a metal rack for clothes.* **racks**

rain |rān| v. To fall in drops of water from clouds: *to rain heavily.* **rains, rained, raining, rainy, rainier, rainiest**

rainy |**rā′nē**| adj. Having rain: *a rainy afternoon.* —**Rainy day**—A time of need in the future. [see *rain*]

ranch |rănch| n. A large farm for raising animals: *herds of cattle at the ranch.* —**Ranch house**—A one-story house. **ranches, rancher**

range |rānj| v. To travel, wander, or roam over a wide area: *will range from place to place.* **ranges, ranged, ranging, ranger, rangers**

ranger |**răn′jər**| n. A person who guards a forest or park: *the park ranger.* [see *range*]

ray |rā| n. A narrow beam of light: *a bright ray.* **rays**

read |rēd| v. To look at something written and understand the meaning: *to read the headlines and the editorials in the newspaper.* **reads, reading, reader, readers**

reader |**rē′dər**| n. A person who reads: *a reader of poetry, plays, and short stories.* [see *read*]

real |**rē′əl**| adj. **1.** True; not made up: *the real story.* **2.** Not imitation or fake: *real flowers.* **really, realize, realist, realistic**

recover |rĭ **kŭv′ər**| v. To get back something lost or stolen: *to recover the missing wallet.* **recovers, recovered, recovering, recovery**

remind |rĭ **mīnd′**| v. To make a person remember something: *to remind him of the meeting.* **reminds, reminded, reminding, reminder**

repair |rĭ **pâr′**| v. To mend or fix: *to repair the damage.* **repairs, repaired, repairing, repairer**

replace |rĭ **plās′**| v. To fill or take the place of: *will replace the exact number of eggs I use.* **replaces, replaced, replacing, replacement**

return |rĭ **tûrn′**| v. To bring, send, put, or give back: *to return the lost wallet.* **returns, returned, returning, returnable**

returning |rĭ tûr′nĭng| *v.* Bringing, sending, putting, or giving back: *was returning what I borrowed.* [see *return*]

reward |rĭ wôrd′| *n.* **1.** Money given or offered for the return of something lost, the capture of a criminal, information, etc.: *received a ten-dollar reward for finding the lost kitten.* **2.** Something given or received in return for doing something; a prize: *got a reward for rescuing the child.* **rewards, rewarded, rewarding**

rich |rĭch| *adj.* Having a lot of money or wealth: *a rich uncle.* **richer, richest, richly, riches**

ripe |rīp| *adj.* Completely grown and ready for eating: *ripe fruit.* **riper, ripest, ripen, ripens, ripened, ripening, ripeness**

river |rĭv′ər| *n.* A natural stream of water that flows into another body of water: *floating down the river.* **rivers**

roar |rôr| *n.* A loud, deep sound: *the animal's roar.* **roars, roared, roaring, roarer**

roll |rōl| *v.* To turn over and over: *to roll the ball across the floor.* **rolls, rolled, rolling, roller**

rolled |rōld| *v.* Turned over and over: *rolled down the stairs.* [see *roll*]

root |ro͞ot| *n.* The part of a plant that grows underground: *dug down to the root.* **roots, rooted, rooting**

rule |ro͞ol| *n.* A statement of what should and should not be done: *one rule of the game.* **rules, ruled, ruling, ruler**

rules |ro͞olz| *n.* More than one rule: *followed the rules.* [see *rule*]

S

sack |săk| *n.* A large bag made of rough cloth: *stuffed dirty clothes into a sack.* **sacks**

saddle |săd′l| *n.* A seat for riding on the back of a horse or similar animal: *a leather saddle.* **saddles, saddled, saddling, saddler**

sail |sāl| *n.* A piece of material that catches the wind to make a boat move: *raised the sail much higher.* **sails, sailed, sailing, sailor**

sank |săngk| *v.* Went under the surface of or to the bottom of some liquid: *sank in the pond.* [see *sink*]

Saturday |săt′ər dā′| *n.* The seventh day of the week: *soccer practice on Saturday.* **Sat.**

save |sāv| *v.* **1.** To set aside or store up for future use: *to save money.* **2.** To rescue or protect from danger: *to save him from the fire.* **saves, saved, saving, savings, saver**

saves |sāvz| *v.* **1.** Sets aside or stores up for future use: *saves all kinds of buttons.* **2.** Rescues or protects from danger: *saves people from burning buildings.* [see *save*]

ă pat / ā pay / â care / ä father / ĕ pet / ē be / ĭ pit / ī pie / î fierce / ŏ pot / ō go / ô paw, for / oi oil / o͞o book / o͞o boot / ou out / ŭ cut / û fur / *th* the / th thin / hw which / zh vision / ə ago, item, pencil, atom, circus
©1977 by Houghton Mifflin Company. Reprinted by permission from THE AMERICAN HERITAGE SCHOOL DICTIONARY.

scale |skāl| *n.* **1.** A series of musical tones: *played a scale on the piano.* **2.** One of the thin, hard parts that covers the outside of fish and reptiles: *a scale from the fish.* **scales, scaled, scaling, scaly**

scold |skōld| *v.* To blame angrily: *to scold for arriving late.* **scolds, scolded, scolding**

score |skôr| *n.* The total points made in a game, test, or contest: *a score of 90.* **scores, scored, scoring, scorer**

scrap |skrăp| *n.* A small piece: *a scrap of paper.* **scraps**

scrape |skrăp| *v.* To smooth or clean by rubbing: *to scrape your boots. n.* A scratched or scraped place: *a scrape on my knee.* **scrapes, scraped, scraping, scraper**

scream |skrēm| *n.* A loud, sharp cry or sound: *heard a scream.* **screams, screamed, screaming, screamer**

scrub |skrŭb| *v.* To wash by rubbing: *to scrub your face.* **scrubs, scrubbed, scrubbing, scrubber**

season |sē'zən| *n.* One of the four parts in a year; spring, summer, fall, or winter: *a snowy season.* **seasons, seasoned, seasoning, seasonal**

seat |sēt| *n.* A place to sit: *an empty seat.* **seats, seated, seating**

second |sĕk'ənd| *n.* One of sixty periods of time in a minute: *lasts only one second. adj.* After the first: *second door on the left.* **seconds, seconded, seconding, secondly**

seem |sēm| *v.* To appear to be: *to seem happy.* **seems, seemed, seeming**

seemed |sēmd| *v.* Appeared to be: *seemed pleased.* [see *seem*]

sense |sĕns| *n.* Good judgment; intelligence: *didn't use very much sense.* **senses, sensed, sensing, senseless**

September |sĕp tĕm'bər| *n.* The ninth month in the year: *the beginning of September.* **Sept.**

seven |sĕv'ən| *adj.* One more than six: *seven cats.* **sevens, seventh, sevenths**

seventh |sĕv'ənth| *adj.* Next after the sixth: *the seventh grade.* [see *seven*]

shake |shāk| *v.* **1.** To move quickly from side to side or up and down: *to shake in the wind.* **2.** To grasp hands in greeting another person: *to shake firmly.* **shakes, shook, shaking, shaky, shakier, shakiest, shakily, shaker**

shame |shām| *n.* A fact to be sorry about: *a shame to miss the party.* **shames, shamed, shaming, shameless, shamelessness, shameful**

shape |shāp| *n.* A form: *the shape of a ball.* **shapes, shaped, shaping, shapeless, shapely**

share |shâr| *n.* A part given or belonging to one person: *an equal share. v.* To divide and give away in parts: *to share an orange.* **2.** To use with others: *will share the same room.* **shares, shared, sharing, sharer**

sharing |shâr'ĭng| *v.* Using with others: *sharing our books.* [see *share*]

shed |shĕd| *n.* A small building used for storage: *tools in the shed.* **sheds, shedding**

sheep |shēp| *n.* An animal with thick wool and hooves: *sheep in the meadow.* **sheepish**

sheet |shēt| *n.* A large piece of cloth used to cover a bed: *slept under the sheet.* **sheets**

shell   sitting

shell |shĕl| *n.* The hard outer covering of some animals: *the turtle's shell.* **shells, shelled, shelling**

she's |shēz| Contraction for *she is: since she's late.*

shine |shīn| *n.* Brightness: *the shine from the flashlight. v.* To make bright; polish: *to shine with a clean cloth.* **shines, shined, shone, shining, shiny, shinier, shiniest**

shining |shī′nĭng| *v.* Making bright; polishing: *is shining shoes. adj.* Bright: *shining star.* [see *shine*]

shirt |shûrt| *n.* A piece of clothing worn on the upper part of the body: *buttoned my shirt.* **shirts**

shock |shŏk| *n.* **1.** A sudden feeling caused by electricity passing through the body: *a shock from the loose wire.* **2.** A sudden, upsetting happening: *was a shock to me.* **shocks, shocked, shocking, shockingly**

shore |shôr| *n.* The land along the edge of an ocean, river, or lake: *shells on the shore.* **shores**

shout |shout| *n.* A loud call or cry: *a shout of joy when the parade began.* **shouts, shouted, shouting**

show |shō| *v.* To put in sight; let be seen: *to show her stamp collection.* **shows, showed, shown, showing**

shower |shou′ər| *n.* **1.** A bath in which water sprays down on a person: *used soap in the shower.* **2.** A brief fall of rain: *an afternoon shower.* **showers, showered, showering**

shown |shōn| *v.* Put in sight; let be seen: *had shown me his new navy-blue coat.* [see *show*]

sidewalk |sīd′wôk′| *n.* A place by the edge of a street where people can walk: *stepped over every big crack in the sidewalk.* **sidewalks**

sideways |sīd′wāz| *adv.* With one side facing forward: *stepped sideways through the crowd.*

silk |sĭlk| *n.* A soft, shiny material: *a jacket lined with silk. adj.* Made of silk: *a silk tie.* **silks, silky, silkier, silkiest, silken**

silver |sĭl′vər| *n.* A soft, shiny white metal: *made of silver. adj.* Shiny gray: *a silver crayon.* **silvers, silvered, silvery**

since |sĭns| *prep.* From a past time until now: *since last month.*

single |sĭng′gəl| *adj.* Only one: *a single sheet of paper.* —**Single file**—A line of people or things arranged one behind the other. **singles, singly, singular**

sink |sĭngk| *v.* To go under the surface of or to the bottom of some liquid: *will sink in the ocean. n.* A shallow tub used for washing: *a sink filled with water.* **sinks, sank, sunk, sunken, sinking**

sir |sûr| *n.* A title used instead of a man's name: *sir or madam.* **sirs**

sit |sĭt| *v.* To rest with the back upright and the weight off the feet: *to sit in a chair.* **sits, sat, sitting, sitter**

sitting |sĭt′ĭng| *v.* Resting upright: *sitting on a bench.* [see *sit*]

ă pat / ā pay / â care / ä father / ĕ pet / ē be / ĭ pit / ī pie / î fierce / ŏ pot / ō go / ô paw, for / oi oil / ŏŏ book / ōō boot / ou out / ŭ cut / û fur / *th* the / th thin / hw which / zh vision / ə ago, item, pencil, atom, circus
©1977 by Houghton Mifflin Company. Reprinted by permission from THE AMERICAN HERITAGE SCHOOL DICTIONARY.

six |sĭks| *adj.* One more than five: *six apples.* **sixes, sixth, sixths**

sixteen |sĭks'tĕn'| *adj.* Six more than ten: *sixteen years old. n.* Six more than ten: *a group of sixteen.* **sixteens, sixteenth**

sixth |sĭksth| *adj.* Next after the fifth: *the sixth person. n.* The next after the fifth: *the sixth in line.* [see *six*]

size |sīz| *n.* **1.** The height, length, and width of something: *the size of our house.* **2.** A series of measurements used for things made, such as clothes: *took a smaller size.* **sizes, sized, sizing**

skate |skāt| *n.* A special shoe that has a metal blade or small wheels for gliding over smooth surfaces: *laced my skate. v.* To move on skates: *to skate in a circle.* **skates, skated, skating, skater**

skating |skā'tĭng| *adj.* Of skating: *skating skirt. v.* Moving on skates: *was skating with friends.* [see *skate*]

skill |skĭl| *n.* The ability to do something well through training and practice: *has skill in spelling.* **skills, skilled, skillful, skillfully, skillfulness**

sleep |slēp| *v.* To rest the body and mind: *to sleep at night.* **sleeps, slept, sleeping, sleepy, sleepier, sleepiest, sleepily, sleeper**

sleepy |slē'pē| *adj.* Needing or ready for sleep: *sleepy child.* [see *sleep*]

slept |slĕpt| *v.* Rested the body and mind: *slept for eight hours.* [see *sleep*]

slice |slīs| *v.* To cut into thin, flat pieces: *to slice meat.* **slices, sliced, slicing, slicer**

sliced |slīst| *adj.* In thin, flat pieces: *ate sliced cheese. v.* Cut into thin, flat pieces: *sliced a loaf of bread.* [see *slice*]

slid |slĭd| *v.* Moved easily: *slid into third base.* [see *slide*]

slide |slīd| *n.* A smooth surface for moving easily on: *a metal slide in the playground. v.* To move easily: *to slide down the hill.* **slides, slid, sliding, slider**

sliding |slī'dĭng| *adj.* Moving easily: *sliding window. v.* Moving easily: *was sliding on skis.* [see *slide*]

slip |slĭp| *v.* To slide suddenly without control: *to slip on the ice.* **slips, slipped, slipping, slippery, slipper, slippers, slipperiness**

slow |slō| *adj.* Not moving quickly: *a slow train on the track.* **slows, slower, slowest, slowed, slowing, slowly, slowness**

slowly |slō'lē| *adv.* Not quickly: *drove slowly.* [see *slow*]

smile |smīl| *v.* To show happiness or amusement: *to smile with delight. n.* An expression on the face showing that a person is happy or amused: *a big smile from every student.* **smiles, smiled, smiling, smiler**

smoke |smōk| *n.* A cloud of gas given off by something burning: *smoke from the fire.* **smokes, smoked, smoking, smoker, smoky, smokier, smokiest**

snap |snăp| *v.* To break with a sudden, sharp sound: *will snap the small twig in half.* **snaps, snapped, snapping, snapper**

sneaker |snē'kər| *n.* A canvas shoe with a rubber sole: *found the matching sneaker.* **sneakers**

sneakers |snē'kərz| *n.* More than one sneaker: *white sneakers for tennis.* [see *sneaker*]

sob |sŏb| *n.* The act or sound of crying with gasps of breath: *heard the child's sob.* *v.* To cry with gasps of breath: *will sob when sad.* **sobs, sobbed, sobbing**

soil |soil| *n.* Dirt: *growing in soil.* **soils, soiled, soiling**

sore |sôr| *adj.* Painful; tender: *soothed my sore toe.* **sores, sorely, sorer, sorest, soreness**

sort |sôrt| *n.* A kind; type: *this sort of animal.* **sorts, sorted, sorting, sorter**

space |spās| *n.* **1.** The region beyond the earth's atmosphere: *a rocket in space.* **2.** A limited place or area: *little space in the tent.* **spaces, spaced, spacing, spacer**

speak |spēk| *v.* To say words: *to speak very softly.* **speaks, spoke, spoken, speaking, speaker**

spend |spěnd| *v.* **1.** To pay out: *will spend five dollars.* **2.** To use up: *to spend more energy.* **spends, spent, spending, spender**

spin |spĭn| *v.* To turn around quickly: *to spin until dizzy.* *n.* A quick turn: *one more spin.* **spins, spun, spinning, spinner**

spoke |spōk| *v.* Said words: *spoke to the teacher.* [see *speak*]

sport |spôrt| *n.* A game in which a person exercises: *the sport of basketball.* **sports, sporting**

stable |stā'bəl| *n.* A building where horses and cattle are kept: *hay in the stable.* **stables, stabled**

stake |stāk| *n.* A stick driven into the ground for holding or marking something: *a stake for the badminton net.* **stakes, staked, staking**

steal |stēl| *v.* To take something that belongs to someone else: *since robbers steal valuables.* **steals, stole, stolen, stealing**

steam |stēm| *n.* Hot water in the form of gas or mist: *steam from the boiling kettle.* **steams, steamed, steaming, steamy, steamer**

steel |stēl| *adj.* Made of steel: *a steel bridge.* *n.* A hard and strong metal: *tools made from steel.* **steels, steely**

steep |stēp| *adj.* Having an almost straight up-and-down slope: *climbed a steep hill.* **steeper, steepest**

stocking |stŏk'ĭng| *n.* A knitted covering for the leg and foot: *wore a silk stocking.* **—In one's stocking feet—**Wearing stockings without shoes. **stockings**

stole |stōl| *v.* Took something dishonestly: *stole money.* [see *steal*]

stories |stôr'ēz| *n.* More than one story: *stories about history.* [see *story*]

story |stôr'ē| *n.* A tale about something that has happened, either true or made up: *a funny story.* **stories**

strange |strānj| *adj.* Unusual; odd: *a strange noise.* **stranger, strangest, strangely, strangeness**

straw |strô| *n.* Dry stalks of grain: *straw for the horses.* **straws**

ă **pat** / ā **pay** / â **care** / ä **father** / ĕ **pet** / ē **be** / ĭ **pit** / ī **pie** / î **fierce** / ŏ **pot** / ō **go** / ô **paw, for** / oi **oil** / o͝o **book** / o͞o **boot** / ou **out** / ŭ **cut** / û **fur** / *th* **the** / th **thin** / hw **which** / zh **vision** / ə **ago, item, pencil, atom, circus**

stream |strēm| *n.* A small body of flowing water: *fished in the stream for large trout.* ***streams, streamed, streaming, streamer***

strike |strīk| *v.* **1.** To stop work for better pay, shorter hours, etc.: *workers who will strike next week.* **2.** To hit: *will strike it with your fist.* **—Strike out—**In baseball, to pitch three strikes to a batter, putting the batter out. ***strikes, struck, striking, striker***

strong |strông| *adj.* Having a great amount of strength or power: *a strong bear.* ***stronger, strongest, strongly***

study |stŭd′ē| *v.* To try to learn: *to study science.* ***studies, studied, studying, studious, student***

sum |sŭm| *n.* **1.** An amount of money: *a sum of five dollars.* **2.** The number gotten from adding two or more numbers together: *to find the sum of 2 plus 6 plus 13.* ***sums, summed, summing, summary***

Sunday |sŭn′dā| *adj.* Of Sunday: *Sunday dinner. n.* The first day of the week: *a picnic on Sunday.* **Sun.**

sure |shŏor| *adj.* Certain: *is sure it will rain.* ***surer, surest, surely***

sweep |swēp| *v.* To clear or take away: *to sweep the dust.* ***sweeps, swept, sweeping, sweeper***

swift |swĭft| *adj.* Moving very fast: *a swift swimmer in the race.* ***swifter, swiftest, swiftly***

swim |swĭm| *v.* To move in water by using arms, legs, or fins: *will swim in the lake.* ***swims, swam, swum, swimming, swimmer***

swing |swĭng| *n.* A seat hung from ropes in which a person can sit and move back and forth: *the swing at the park.* ***swings, swung, swinging, swinger***

sword |sôrd| *n.* A weapon with a long sharp blade attached to a handle: *the knight's sword.* ***swords***

T

team |tēm| *n.* A group of people playing or working together: *a hockey team.* ***teams, teamed, teaming***

tear |tîr| *n.* A drop of liquid coming from the eye: *wiped away a tear.* ***tears, teared, tearing, tearful***

tear |târ| *v.* To make a hole by ripping: *to tear a sleeve.* ***tears, tore, torn, tearing***

teeth |tēth| *n.* More than one tooth: *white teeth.* [see *tooth*]

tend |tĕnd| *v.* To be likely: *to tend to sleep late.* ***tends, tended, tending, tender***

thick |thĭk| *adj.* Having much space between two sides: *thick doors and walls.* **—Through thick and thin—**In both good and bad times. ***thicker, thickest, thickly, thickness***

thousand |thou′zənd| *adj.* Ten times one hundred: *earned a thousand dollars.* ***thousands, thousandth***

thread |thrĕd| *n.* Thin strands, or lengths, of spun and twisted cotton, silk, nylon, etc., used for sewing: *blue thread for sewing the shirt.* ***threads, threaded, threading, threader***

throw |thrō| *n.* A toss: *a throw to the catcher.* *v.* To send through the air; toss: *will throw the ball.* **throws, threw, thrown, throwing, thrower**

ticket |tĭk′ĭt| *n.* **1.** A card or paper that gives certain rights to the person who holds it: *a ticket to the circus.* **2.** A tag or label attached to something to show a price, tell who owns it, etc.: *a ticket sewn on a shirt.* **tickets, ticketed, ticketing**

tin |tĭn| *n.* A soft silver-white metal: *a box made of tin.* **tins, tinned, tinning, tinny**

tiny |tī′nē| *adj.* Very small: *a tiny kitten.* **tinier, tiniest**

tire |tīr| *v.* To make or become weary: *to tire after running.* **tires, tired, tiring, tireless, tiresome**

tired |tīrd| *adj.* Weary, or worn out: *too tired to stay awake.* [see *tire*]

ton |tŭn| *n.* A unit of weight equal to 2,000 pounds: *weighed a ton.* **tons**

tooth |tōōth| *n.* One of the hard, bony parts in the mouth, used for chewing and biting: *one loose tooth.* **teeth, toothy**

tore |tôr| *v.* Made a hole by ripping: *tore the cloth.* [see *tear*]

tower |tou′ər| *n.* A tall building: *the bell in the tower.* **towers, towered, towering**

trace |trās| *n.* **1.** A small amount: *a trace of dirt.* **2.** A drawing done by tracing: *a trace of the circle.* *v.* To copy by drawing over lines seen through thin paper: *to trace a picture.* **traces, traced, tracing, tracer**

trap |trăp| *n.* A trick used to catch a person by surprise: *a sneaky trap.* **traps, trapped, trapping, trapper**

tribe |trīb| *n.* A group of people with the same ancestors and traditions: *from the same tribe.* **tribes, tribal**

trick |trĭk| *n.* A clever or skillful act: *the dog's new trick.* **tricks, tricked, tricking, tricky, trickier, trickiest, trickster**

trim |trĭm| *v.* To make neat by cutting away unnecessary parts: *to trim the plants.* **trims, trimmed, trimming, trimmer**

trust |trŭst| *n.* A strong belief in someone's honesty, truthfulness, power, etc.: *has your trust.* **trusts, trusted, trusting, trustful, trustless, trustiness**

Tuesday |tōōz′dā′| *adj.* Of Tuesday: *a Tuesday meeting.* *n.* The third day of the week: *will mail by Tuesday.* **Tues.**

turtle |tûr′tl| *n.* A reptile with a round body enclosed in a hard shell: *a turtle in the pond.* **turtles**

twenty |twĕn′tē| *adj.* Two times ten: *twenty minutes ago.* **twenties, twentieth**

twenty-five |twĕn′tē fīv′| *adj.* Five more than twenty: *counted twenty-five times.* **twenty-fives, twenty-fifth**

U

unlock |ŭn lŏk′| *v.* To open the lock of: *hard to unlock.* [see *lock*]

ă pat / ā pay / â care / ä father / ĕ pet / ē be / ĭ pit / ī pie / î fierce / ŏ pot / ō go / ô paw, for / oi oil / ŏŏ book / ōŏ boot / ou out / ŭ cut / û fur / *th* the / th thin / hw which / zh vision / ə ago, item, pencil, atom, circus
©1977 by Houghton Mifflin Company. Reprinted by permission from THE AMERICAN HERITAGE SCHOOL DICTIONARY.

until |ŭn tĭl'| *conj.* Up to the time when: *until it freezes. prep.* Up to the time of: *slept until noon.*

■■■■■ **W** ■■■■■

wade |wād| *v.* To walk slowly and with difficulty through water, mud, or snow: *to wade across the stream. n.* A slow and difficult walk: *a wade into the ocean.* **wades, waded, wading**

wait |wāt| *v.* To stay in a place until something happens or someone comes: *to wait for the bus.* **waits, waited, waiting, waiter, waitress**

waiting |wā'tĭng| *v.* Staying until something happens or someone comes: *waiting for the rain to stop.* [see *wait*]

wake |wāk| *v.* To stop sleeping: *to wake at seven o'clock.* **wakes, waked, woke, waking, waken, wakens, wakened, wakening**

waste |wāst| *n.* Material to be thrown away; garbage: *threw the waste into a bag.* **wastes, wasted, wasting, wasteful, wastefully, waster**

weak |wēk| *adj.* Not having power; faint: *a weak sound.* **weaker, weakest, weakly, weakness**

wear |wâr| *v.* To have on or put on the body: *to wear a coat.* **wears, wore, worn, wearing**

Wednesday |wĕnz'dā'| *n.* The fourth day of the week: *stayed until Wednesday.* **Wed.**

weekend |wēk'ĕnd'| *n.* The time between Friday night and Sunday night: *a weekend away from home.* **weekends**

wheel |wēl| *n.* **1.** Something shaped or used like a wheel: *to steer with the wheel.* **2.** A ring, either solid or with spokes, that turns on its center: *the wheel on the old covered wagon.* **wheels, wheeled, wheeling**

whip |wĭp| *n.* A flexible strap attached to a handle: *snapped the whip. v.* To beat eggs, batter, etc.: *will whip a dozen eggs.* **whips, whipped, whipping**

wind |wīnd| *v.* To wrap or fold around something: *to wind yarn into a ball.* **winds, wound, winding**

wind |wīnd| *n.* Air that is moving: *knocked down by the wind.* **windy, windier, windiest, winds**

windy |wĭn'dē| *adj.* Having much wind: *a windy day.* [see *wind*]

woke |wōk| *v.* Stopped sleeping: *woke late in the day.* [see *wake*]

woman |woŏm'ən| *n.* An adult female human being: *the woman with black hair.* **women, womanly**

women |wĭm'ĭn| *n.* More than one woman: *talking with the women in our town.* [see *woman*]

won't |wōnt| Contraction for *will not: won't finish on time.*

wore |wôr| *v.* Had on or put on the body: *wore a heavy sweater under my jacket.* [see *wear*]

worn |wôrn| *v.* Had on or put on the body: *the shirt you had worn yesterday. adj.* Damaged because of use or wear: *worn, dirty shirt.* [see *wear*]

worry |wûr'ē| *v.* To feel or cause to feel troubled or uneasy: *to worry them by coming home late.* **worries, worried, worrying, worrier**

worth |wûrth| *n.* Value, usefulness, or importance: *gems of great worth.* **worthy, worthless, worthlessness, worthiness**

wound |wound| *adj.* Wrapped or folded around: *wound tightly.* —|wo͞ond| *n.* An injury or hurt: *a knee wound.* [see *wind*]

wrap |răp| *v.* To cover with paper and tie up: *will wrap the gift.* **wraps, wrapped, wrapping, wrapper**

write |rīt| *v.* **1.** To form words or symbols with a pen, pencil, or other instrument: *to write your name.* **2.** To make up stories, books, poems, or articles: *to write for the newspaper.* **writes, wrote, writing, written, writer, writers**

writer |rī′tər| *n.* A person who writes; an author: *a writer of mysteries.* [see *write*]

wrong |rông| *adj.* Not correct: *gave me the wrong answer.* **wrongs, wronged, wronging, wrongly**

Y

yard |yärd| *n.* **1.** An area of ground around a house or other building: *played outside in the yard.* **2.** An area used for a certain kind of business: *a coal yard.* **yards, yardage**

yellow |yĕl′ō| *adj.* Having the color yellow: *a yellow sweater. n.* The color of lemons and gold: *leaves of yellow and red.* **yellows, yellowed, yellowing**

ă pat / ā pay / â care / ä father / ĕ pet / ē be / ĭ pit / ī pie / î fierce / ŏ pot / ō go / ô paw, for / oi oil / o͝o book / o͞o boot / ou out / ŭ cut / û fur / *th* the / th thin / hw which / zh vision / ə ago, item, pencil, atom, circus